The Ethics of Genetic Engineering

ISSUES
(previously Issues for the Nineties)

Volume 12

Editor

Craig Donnellan

Independence

Educational Publishers

First published by Independence
PO Box 295
Cambridge CB1 3XP
England

British Library Cataloguing in Publication Data
The Ethics of Genetic Engineering – (Issues Series)
I. Donnellan, Craig II. Series
174.2'5

ISBN 1 86168 043 0

Printed in Great Britain
City Print Ltd
Milton Keynes

Typeset by
Claire Boyd

Cover
The illustration on the front cover is by
Michaela Bloomfield.

CONTENTS

Introduction

The Ethics of Genetic Engineering is the twelfth volume in the series: **Issues**. The aim of this series is to offer up-to-date information about important issues in our world.

The Ethics of Genetic Engineering looks at the cloning debate, genetically modified foods and genetic testing.

The information comes from a wide variety of sources and includes:
Government reports and statistics
Newspaper reports and features
Magazine articles and surveys
Literature from lobby groups
and charitable organisations.

It is hoped that, as you read about the many aspects of the issues explored in this book, you will critically evaluate the information presented. It is important that you decide whether you are being presented with facts or opinions. Does the writer give a biased or an unbiased report? If an opinion is being expressed, do you agree with the writer?

The Ethics of Genetic Engineering offers a useful starting-point for those who need convenient access to information about the many issues involved. However, it is only a starting-point. At the back of the book is a list of organisations which you may want to contact for further information.

*****

Modern biotechnology

Information from *foodfuture*, an initiative of the Food and Drink Federation

Moral and ethical considerations

Research shows that consumers' moral beliefs influence their attitudes towards applications of modern biotechnology.

The moral and ethical concerns which have been raised about modern biotechnology and were the focus of discussion at the Review Conference arise from unease that:

It interferes with the workings of nature and creation

Has man the right 'to play God' by introducing unnatural processes into the evolutionary system? The transfer of genetic material between species is disrespectful – although there is less moral objection to transfer of genes between plants and microbes than between animals and humans.

Response: If interfering with God's created order is unnatural, then all agricultural and medical processes are unnatural. Individuals have the right to their religious and moral beliefs and must work out their own positions.

'If one is a Christian, a vegetarian, is Jewish, Muslim or believes in organic food, one has actually a considerably different approach to ethical issues.'
Dr Julian Kinderlerer
Assistant Director, Institute of Biotechnological Law and Ethics, University of Sheffield

'We will not stock anything which would allow human material to enter the food chain. We have grave doubts about trans-genetics between animals and plants but, leaving those aside, we will stock genetically engineered products if they can be shown to be safe, effective, reliable and provide a consumer benefit.'
Mr Bill Shannon
General Manager Co-op
Brand, CWS Retail

foodfuture

It takes irresponsible risks

Irresponsible risks are taken which could lead to harmful consequences. Products which are released into the environment may not be controllable and this could lead to indestructible weeds, resistance to pests and herbicides and to loss of genetic diversity.

Response: The possible harmful effects are speculative. Scientists claim that the technology is safer than traditional methods because it is more precise in its targeting.

Controls can reduce risks. Stringent regulations and monitoring are in place.

'We have regulations and the key issue is to ensure safety to humans and the environment. We must have regulation that does take account of experience, can be changed and is changed as it is deemed appropriate because of the experience gained. We must not lose sight of the international dimension. We are looking at global trade in biotech-nology products and there needs to be a global system to take account of that.'
Dr Helen Marquard
Biotechnology Unit,
Department of the Environment

'Choice – of the type of food, of having a future world food supply and of having a sustainable environment to live in – is only of value if it is based on trust: trust of the scientist, of the Government and of the appropriate regulatory authorities. All we can seek

NO JOSH, THE PARABLE OF THE LOAVES AND FISHES IS **NOT** AN EXAMPLE OF CLONING!

to do is minimise the risk, we cannot eliminate it. This must be based on the best knowledge.'

Mr Ben Gill
Deputy President,
National Farmers' Union

'Monitoring seems to be conspicuously lacking in what happens. We don't know what happens to these genetically modified organisms over a period of time.'

Sir Crispin Tickell
Warden, Green College,
Oxford; Chairman, Government
panel on sustainable development

'We at FDF cannot provide the objective research into the long-term safety of biological applications which is so badly needed. I would urge the Government to reconsider its current plans for reducing research expenditure in this area.'

Mr Guy Walker, CBE
President, Food and Drink
Federation; Chairman, Van Den
Bergh Foods Ltd

It exploits and harms the economically vulnerable

Classifying genetic materials as patentable puts living organisms on the same level as objects which can be invented and owned. Large corporations with patent rights will exploit the resources of developing countries and damage their economies and their small farmers.

Little has been done to apply the new technology in areas with food shortages.

Response: Patents are necessary to encourage research and development as they provide a return on investment and a fair reward and protection for innovative work. They do not, however, give moral rights.

All new technologies have far-reaching socio-economic effects. Initially they tend to benefit developed countries which have the resources for research and development.

'The world's starving do not make good customers. This is not intended as a criticism of the corporate sector which bears no greater responsibility for feeding the hungry than the rest of us. But,

please, stop promoting biotechnology as a technical fix for hunger. It is misleading since it ignores all the other underlying causes of starvation.'

Ms Julie Sheppard
Consultant, Genetics Forum

'When are we going to benefit the world with this marvellous technology? What benefits can we expect it to bring to world hunger?'

Ms Maeve Robertson
Member, MAFF
Consumer Panel

It is unfair to animals

There are ethical and welfare concerns about using animals in research which causes them pain, suffering or distress. Modern biotechnology will open up a new era in exploitation of animals in which morality will give way to expediency.

Response: Procedures which cause pain and suffering to farm animals are open to moral criticism. This technology should not be singled out from other methods of breeding and farming animals, particularly as it has the potential to improve animal welfare. When working with animals, scientists conform with strict procedures laid down by government.

'We have to realise that genetic selection has caused massive suffering. The food industry should realise that animals have a capacity to suffer, to feel pain, fear, stress and joy. The food industry and the scientists should know about it.'

Mrs Irene Williams, Director,
Compassion in World Farming

'If (in the future) there are ever genetically modified animals in the farm environment, I can assure you MAFF will be applying the animal welfare legislation we have for farm animals as strictly and as strongly as we do in all other respects.'

Mr Stewart Marshall
Ministry of Agriculture,
Fisheries and Food (MAFF)

'The NFU believes that Government should ensure that any genetic engineering of farm animals does not lead to animal welfare problems. It is of paramount importance that consumers have confidence in the food they eat and how it has been produced.'

Mr Ross Kenyon
Member, National Farmers'
Union Biotechnology Working Party

• The above is an extract from *Modern biotechnology*, produced by foodfuture, an initiative of the Food and Drink Federation. See page 41 for address details.   © *foodfuture*

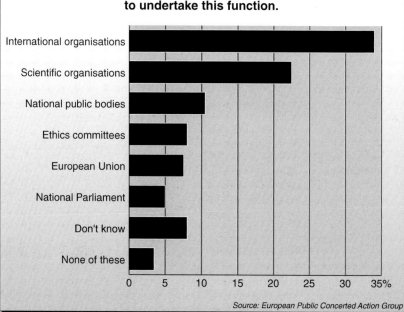

Who should regulate biotechnology?

The Eurobarometer on Biotechnology was conducted during October and November, 1996. The total sample within the EU was 16,246 respondents (about 1,000 per EU country). People were asked which of a selection of bodies they thought best placed to undertake this function.

Source: European Public Concerted Action Group

Hello Dolly

She looks exactly like any other sheep. But the cloning method used to produce Dolly may change our lives. Roger Highfield reports

The possibility that an adult human can be cloned from a single blood or skin cell was raised yesterday with the announcement that scientists have produced the world's first clone of an adult animal.

The clone, a Finn Dorset sheep called Dolly, paves the way to unprecedented genetic manipulation of farmyard animals, more cheaply and more accurately than ever before.

A single cell could be taken from a prize bull, elite racehorse or award-winning pig, and hundreds of identical animals produced using the patented cloning technology developed at the Roslin Institute and PPL Therapeutics, near Edinburgh.

Introduction or deletion of genes in the cloned cells also offers the means to make animals that produce drugs in their milk, grow faster for meat production, or are resistant to diseases such as scrapie and BSE.

The first sheep altered using the method may be born later this year though it will be several years before scientists will have developed the means to alter many genes simultaneously, which will be necessary to boost growth or make leaner beef.

But any other use of the technology, for instance to mass-produce human eggs for use in in-vitro fertilisation, is outlawed, said Dr Ron James, managing director of PPL.

Dr James said he had advised relevant regulatory committees about the development and its implications but added: 'An Act of Parliament specifically forbids even doing with human eggs what we have done with sheep eggs.'

And he acknowledged that there are limitations to the use of the technology at the farm – herds of identical livestock are at greater risk of disease – in addition to the inevitable qualms about mass-producing identical animals or designing animals for human use.

In earlier work, the Roslin team unveiled Megan and Morag, sheep that had been cloned by taking a cell from an early embryo, mass-producing it in the laboratory, and using these cells to 'reprogram' two emptied eggs.

Until now it has been thought impossible to perform the same feat using cells from an adult animal. Unlike embryo cells, which have the potential to develop into a vast range of cell types, adult cells are differentiated, that is they have turned into a liver, brain or, in this case, a cell from the udder.

Dr Ian Wilmut, Dr Keith Campbell, and Dr Jim McWhir at Edinburgh's Roslin Institute, working with Angelica Schnieke and Dr Alex Kind at PPL Therapeutics, will announce the feat this week in the journal *Nature*, cloning cells from the mammary gland and connective tissue.

This breakthrough, the first time that any new-born mammal has been derived from adult cells, offers PPL the possibility of using the technique to alter genetically sheep much more easily than before.

Previously, scientists have used a hit-and-miss affair: injecting DNA into an embryo and hoping that it is taken up, which only happens in 10 per cent of cases or less.

Instead, genes can be introduced into large numbers of cloned cells. Then the cells where genetic engineering has been successful are selected and mass-produced, producing a herd of identical 'transgenic' animals.

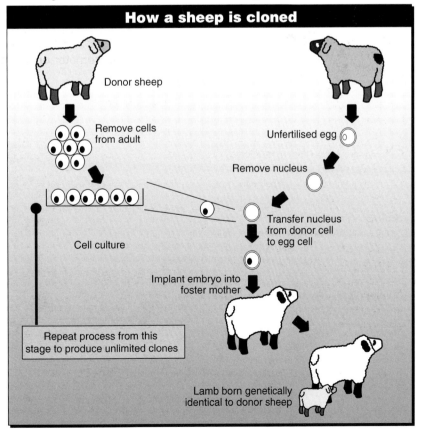

How a sheep is cloned

Donor sheep

Remove cells from adult

Cell culture

Unfertilised egg

Remove nucleus

Transfer nucleus from donor cell to egg cell

Implant embryo into foster mother

Repeat process from this stage to produce unlimited clones

Lamb born genetically identical to donor sheep

'We are looking at things like introducing genes for blood-clotting proteins that haemophiliacs lack,' said Dr James, adding that they focused on cloning mammary cells to make it easier to ensure that human proteins will be made in the animal's milk.

Moreover, the technique also enables the team to knock out genes, raising the possibility of deleting the prion protein – one linked to BSE – from cows so they are resistant to the disease. 'Cloning cattle should be possible, because the embryology is not too dissimilar to sheep,' he said, adding that pigs would also be studied.

Cloning from adult animals may be more useful to agriculture than cloning from embryos, as farmers will be able to pick particularly productive and disease-resistant adult animals to copy.

In this case, the resulting lamb – Dolly – was genetically identical to the sheep from which the cell was taken. Dolly is now several months old and is showing every sign of normal development.

'Animal breeding companies are already showing interest in the use of this technology to multiply their best animals,' said Roslin team leader Dr Ian Wilmut. 'Genetic modification of the donor cells in culture before they are used in nuclear transfer will also allow us to introduce very precise changes in their DNA and open up the possibilities for a range of new products for the treatment of, for example, cancers and inflammation. What this will mostly be used for is to produce more health care products. It will enable us to study genetic diseases for which there is presently no cure and track down the mechanisms that are involved. The next step is to use the cells in culture in the lab and target genetic changes into that culture.'

The Roslin Institute has agreed to grant PPL an exclusive licence for the use of the technology to make human protein drugs. Patents to protect the new technology have been applied for.

Previous efforts to clone Megan and Morgan from embryo cells ran into problems. Six in every 10 attempts made in the original experiments worked. Five clones were produced but three sisters died – two within minutes of birth and the third within 10 days.

Post-mortem examinations revealed kidney and cardiovascular abnormalities.

How a sheep is cloned

A way to 'reprogram' an egg cell with the genetic material from one of millions of identical cells grown in the laboratory lies at the heart of the method.

The research demonstrates the ability to take cells from the mammary tissue of sheep, mass-produce these and then take the part containing the genetic code – the nucleus – and transfer it into an egg that has had its nucleus removed.

Once the mammary cells has been removed, the efforts to turn them into identical cells mark one of the most important achievements because it is a 'clone', a collection – which can be made as large as one likes – of genetically identical cells growing in a glass dish.

The DNA from this clone was used to re-program an unfertilised egg, obtained by stimulating a ewe with fertility drugs.

The team removed the chromosomes of the egg while leaving as much as possible of the remaining fat-speckled transparent jelly intact.

Into the transparent outer casing of the egg was pushed the cloned cell. The cell was squirted alongside the much larger dollop – the egg's chromosome – stripped jelly that is in an inner, fine membrane.

The egg was then placed between two electrodes and a direct electric current passed across it, a step that perforates the membranes separating the cell and egg so the contents can fuse to begin the biochemistry of life.

The egg, implanted into a surrogate mother, then developed as normal.

© Telegraph Group Limited, London 1997

Scientist of 'Dolly the sheep' fame asked by families to clone their close relatives

By Tim Radford, Science Editor

The leader of the team that stunned the world by cloning Dolly the sheep said last night he had been asked by two families to produce exact genetic copies of relatives.

Ian Wilmut, of the Roslin Institute, near Edinburgh, told a news conference organised by the American Association for the Advancement of Science in Washington that he had said no. 'I can't think of any embryologist who would be interested in cloning a human being.

'One inquiry was from a lady shortly to lose her father and the other was from a couple who lost their daughters in an automobile accident.'

He did not say where the requests had come from. Almost a decade ago the Roslin Institute genetically engineered a sheep to produce a human hormone needed by cystic fibrosis sufferers. In 1996 scientists cloned two lambs, called Megan and Morag, from a laboratory embryo cell line as part of research into accurate genetic manipulation.

But it was Dolly the sheep who in February provoked execration and admiration. They took a cell from the mammary gland of a six-year-old sheep and produced an exact copy.

Every cell contains the DNA code for the whole creature but shortly after conception, cells specialise. The Roslin team had made this process go backwards.

Dr Wilmut said: 'I share the concern, almost universal, that this technique should not be misused.'

© The Guardian
June, 1997

Now meet Polly, a clone with human genes

Sheep may provide drugs and transplant organs

The world's first cloned sheep containing human genes was unveiled yesterday by the team responsible for Dolly.

Polly and four other cloned lambs mark a milestone in the effort to alter the genetic make-up of animals. It is hoped that similar animals will eventually provide human drugs, milk and transplant organs as well as aiding medical research.

In the aftermath of the emergence of Dolly, the first cloned sheep, earlier this year, futuristic debate about cloning humans eclipsed the immediate implications and concerns about the ease with which it will be possible to make Polly and other so-called 'transgenic' animals.

Yesterday's announcement, by PPL Therapeutics and the Roslin Institute near Edinburgh, will intensify pressure from animal rights campaigners to study the welfare of transgenic animals and examine the ethics of tailoring animals for human use.

Analysis by Roslin scientists confirms that Polly, who was born on July 9, carries a human gene responsible for a 'therapeutic protein', one that she will produce in her milk in large volumes by the standards of the pharmaceutical industry.

Now a flock of identical sheep can be made and the protein extracted and used as a drug. However, the team was not specific about the protein, or its role, because making these details public would jeopardise publication of its research.

Scientists hope that one day sheep like Polly and transgenic cows will secrete in their milk everything from human antithrombin III, a protein that helps to stop blood clotting, to human albumin, which is used in the treatment of burns.

*By Roger Highfield,
Science Editor*

'Nuclear transfer technology' – the method of cloning an adult animal used for the first time to make Dolly – holds the promise of making the genetic manipulation of animals easier than ever. Polly is the first demonstration that the method will work.

'I am delighted to see our collaborative efforts moving so rapidly towards useful medical applications,' said Dr Ian Wilmut of the Roslin Institute and head of the team that produced Dolly.

Prof Grahame Bulfield, Roslin Institute director, added: 'The pioneering work will stimulate new opportunities in both agricultural and biomedical research.'

Apart from turning sheep into drug factories, the introduction or deletion of genes in the cloned cells also offers the means to make animals that grow faster for meat production, that are resistant to diseases such as scrapie, that have 'humanised' organs for transplant, or even that produce human milk.

However, as the journal *Nature* commented yesterday, there is increasing pressure for an inquiry into the production and use of transgenic animals. Scientists are uncertain of the long-term effects.

The technology is also being used to make animals designed to suffer human-like diseases for testing treatments.

PPL has already been given permission to use another sheep-derived human protein – alpha-1-antitrypsin – to help prevent lung damage in patients with cystic fibrosis.

The sheep that make this protein in their milk were made by inefficient traditional genetic engineering methods.

Polly and her sisters demonstrate the commercial potential of cloning that will lead to a wide range of transgenic animals more quickly and easily than ever.

"BA... BAAAAA..."

THE SHEEP ORGAN TRANSPLANT WAS A COMPLETE SUCCESS

Ken Pyne

Existing genetic engineering methods are a hit-and-miss affair: injecting DNA into an embryo and hoping that it is taken up, which only happens in 10 per cent of cases or less. Overall, of 10,000 eggs injected with foreign DNA, only three make it to adulthood. Polly was made in a different way. She started out as tissue taken from a Poll Dorset sheep, hence her name.

Copies of the fibroblast cells in connective tissue taken from the donor were grown in the laboratory, then human genes, labelled with a marker, were introduced.

First the team selected the cloned cells labelled with the marker, then they analysed which of those had the human gene.

Nuclei of the selected cells –

Polly and four other cloned lambs mark a milestone in the effort to alter the genetic make-up of animals

the part containing the genetic instructions for the Poll Dorset sheep and the human protein – were used to 'reprogram' sheep's eggs from which the DNA had been removed.

The resulting embryos were transplanted into Scottish Blackface ewes and pregnancies established. The success rate was better than that used to make Dolly, where only one

of 277 attempts survived. Dr James said that this showed that introduction of a human gene had not affected the process.

Blood samples were taken from the resulting lambs and used to confirm the presence of the added genes. Of the five lambs, one – Polly – has the human gene plus a marker gene. Two more are expected to carry human genes, while the final two have only the marker gene.

Dr Alan Colman, research director of PPL, said: 'These lambs are the realisation of our vision to produce instant flocks or herds that express high concentrations of valuable therapeutic proteins very quickly.'

Dolly's creator: humans can be cloned

Scientists could be producing human clones in less than two years, the man who created Dolly the sheep admitted yesterday.

Geneticist Dr Ian Wilmut said a huge research effort, using 'thousands' of human eggs, would be needed to perfect the techniques.

But he told a Commons inquiry: 'I'm sure if we wanted to do it, it could be done. If a scientist were prepared to make that effort, there could be much significant progress in one or two years.'

Dr Wilmut insisted that his team at the Roslin Institute in Edinburgh, who cloned Dolly from an adult sheep, were 'unanimously' opposed to such experiments and would welcome a ban on them.

His revelation drew warnings from MPs that science could be on the verge of a terrifying phase in human engineering. 'This sort of stuff is straight out of the Nazis and Dr Joseph Mengele tinkering with Hitler clones in the Amazonian jungle,' one Labour MP said privately.

Professor Graham Bulfield,

By Benedict Brogan, Political Reporter

director of the Roslin Institute, told the Commons Science and Technology Select Committee there could be extreme circumstances in which a scientist 'somewhere in the world' might attempt to clone a human being. But both men claimed that human experiments using the technology developed by Roslin were remote and unlikely. Dr Wilmut said: 'We can see no reason why anyone would want to make a copy of a person.'

News of Dolly's existence has sparked world-wide concern and calls for strict rules to prevent genetic abuses by unscrupulous scientists.

Yet the Human Fertilisation and Embryology Authority, which regulates genetic engineering in Britain, has stopped short of slamming the door on human cloning experiments.

Its chairman Ruth Deach told the Commons inquiry that there was

a possibility the research might be of benefit in the future.

'We wish to find a way forward that produces benefits but steers well clear of the production of identical human beings without a father just to serve somebody else's ends.'

Liberal Democrat MP David Alton, who has tabled a Commons motion calling for the immediate suspension of cloning experiments, criticised the HFEA's attitude yesterday.

He said: 'This is a British development and we should be at the forefront of efforts to stop it.

'There is already evidence of the law being broken here, and I'm sure you will find incidents of scientists tempted to experiment in many parts of the world.'

Gay activists in the US are fighting plans to outlaw human cloning, saying they see it as a 'defence' against possible future moves to track down and eliminate a 'homosexual gene'.

Mighty mouse

It's a cartoon concept, but the implications are scientifically exciting – and ethically disturbing

American scientists have produced rippling rodents – with muscles three times bigger than normal and 30 per cent larger overall – by knocking out a gene which controls muscle growth.

The same technique could be used to create super races of giant farmyard animals, all yielding huge quantities of meat.

But the research has also raised the ethically disturbing spectre of genetic engineering in humans to create super athletes.

If scientists can disable the same growth gene in adults, the skinniest beanpoles could become Arnold Schwarzenegger lookalikes.

Animal rights campaigners immediately condemned the research, claiming it would lead to 'farmyards of suffering and cruelty'.

They warned that selective breeding of chickens, cows and pigs had already produced animals unable to bear their own body weight.

But scientists insist the breakthrough could have tremendous implications for the treatment of muscle-wasting diseases such as muscular dystrophy. Some specialists believe it could also lead to ways of combating disability caused by muscle deterioration as people age.

Despite their deformed appearance and super strength, the mice, now a year old, appear to be perfectly healthy.

British geneticists said the discovery was 'extremely exciting', but warned it could take years before the technique benefited mankind. 'There are very possibly some interesting medical implications,' said geneticist Professor Steve Jones, of University College London. One could visualise the possibility of producing a drug which interferes with this growth factor and causes muscles to grow more.

By David Derbyshire, Science Correspondent

'The farming business is very interested in this type of work, although the interesting thing will be whether the public accepts it.'

> ### If scientists can disable the same growth gene in adults, the skinniest beanpoles could become Arnold Schwarzenegger lookalikes

Others warned that the technology could be abused in the race to find more effective steroids. Dr Richard Nicholson, editor of the *Bulletin of Medical Ethics*, said: 'The potential for abuse would be right there from the start.'

To create the mutant rodents, researchers took cells from a mouse embryo and used chemicals to knock out a newly-discovered gene called GDF8, the science journal *Nature* reports today.

The gene contains the blueprint for the chemical myostatin, which controls the development of muscles in most mammals. The altered cells were cloned and then injected into normal mice embryos. After being implanted in surrogate mothers, they grew into mutant offspring.

'The first thing we noticed was that the knockout mice had unusually large shoulders and hips,' said geneticist Dr Alexandra McPherron. 'On closer analysis, we found that all their muscles were two to three times normal size.'

Researchers have already identified the human version of the GDF8 gene and are investigating whether it does the same job. Team leader Dr Se-Jin Lee said: 'We are excited that GDF8 could give us new opportunities to treat the many muscle-wasting diseases like muscular dystrophy or cachexia, the muscle loss that accompanies some cancers and AIDS.

'We've also found GDF8 in chickens and cows so we might be able to interfere with it to create livestock with more meat and relatively less fat.'

But campaigners for cruelty-free farming claim that creating super strains of animals is unethical and unnecessary.

Dr Tim O'Brien, head of research at Compassion in World Farming, said: 'This sort of work, which involves invasive surgery, has a high potential for animal suffering and we would want it to be stopped.'

© The Daily Mail
May, 1997

Cloning is killing

Making clones is to be legalised in America. Hugo Gurdon, Washington Correspondent, argues that it will mean the taking of human life

As you read this, scientists in America are cloning humans – not breathing, walking people, of course, but human life nevertheless.

Cells are dividing and subdividing in laboratory dishes, nuclei are being extracted and transferred, and their creators are triumphant about it: 'Who's going to stop us?' asked Dr Masood Khatamee, of the Fertility Research Foundation, yesterday.

The answer is: not Washington. In February, after scientists in Edinburgh created a sheep called Dolly using just one cell of another sheep, President Clinton ordered the National Bioethics Advisory Commission urgently to study the implications. What should be done, he wanted to know, now that technology existed which could enable us to manufacture a living replica of another human?

Tomorrow, the commission will hold a public meeting to give a sort of answer. Sort of, because it has avoided the central moral question about whether humankind should arrogate the power of creation.

The *Washington Post* has revealed that the commission will seek a ban on the use of duplicate embryos to produce cloned babies – for infertile women, for example – but it will not recommend any restriction on cloning by private laboratories for other medical research. Scientists claim their work could soon produce cures for diabetes, spinal cord injuries, and even cancer, and the possibility of attaining such medical prizes has proved persuasive. So has the less admirable view, expressed by Dr Masood Khatamee, that 'if we stop it in this country, other parts of the world will be ahead of us'. Arguing that we must do something which may be wrong to make sure others do not do it better

is like suggesting we refine the techniques of repression to make sure we stay ahead of North Korea.

Those who support human cloning are asking society to agree that there is nothing wrong with replicating embryos, letting them develop for an unspecified period until they reach scientific usefulness, and then, after they have been experimented on, killing them. There is every reason why this should make us morally queasy.

The commission deserves sympathy, for it was given only four months in which to exercise the judgement of Solomon. Unfortunately, it has not exercised judgement; rather, it has sought to split the difference between mutually exclusive propositions. It has addressed the most easily understood nightmare – the production of cloned babies – and recommended that the Government prevent it. But it has not answered the questions raised by one of the commission members, Thomas Murray, the director of the Centre for Biomedical Ethics at Case Western Reserve University, who said cloning 'really goes to the heart of what's significant about having children, being a parent, the interweaving of generations and . . . Whether [it] is elevating narcissism to new heights.'

With cloning, as with abortion, it is difficult to discern any logical compromise between either accepting or rejecting the inviolability of human life. If you believe that there is a moral difference between a

---

'If we stop it in this country, other parts of the world will be ahead of us'

---

human at, say, two weeks' gestation and one at two months', you have not compromised: you have become a partisan.

The artificial replication of human life is not something that can be half-done. In moral terms, it is not a rheostat which can be turned to any desired point on a sliding scale. Or rather, it is like a rheostat in one alarming way; rheostats are adjusted from time to time as desired. Steve Jones, professor of genetics at University College London, argued in this newspaper in March that ethics always follow science. That is precisely the danger. Once we accept limited forms of cloning, the temptation to allow more would gradually become harder to resist.

Our civilisation is founded upon Judaeo-Christian morality, at the centre of which are the dignity, character and individuality of every human being. To worry about human cloning, it is not necessary to conjure fantastical and horrific visions of a future world in which tyrants such as Saddam Hussein replicate themselves. It is necessary only to recognise that the new wonder-science, which promises so much, may yet be another blow against our humanity.

How can we be diminished, some people will ask, by allowing medical science the freedom to find cures for grievous illnesses? The answer is that our humanity is not coterminous with our physical well-being or our freedom from anxiety about inherited disease. It is there in out traditional respect for human life, which cannot be bent to the point where we accept the production and culling of some human life for the benefit of other human beings. If we diminish humanity to the point where it is manipulated in a Petri dish, we diminish ourselves.

Why Dolly the clone is cause for hope, not horror

After the hysteria, a considered view of mankind's great debate. By Professor Robert Winston, Professor of fertility studies, Hammersmith Hospital, London

The debate over cloning burst into life with the birth of Dolly the lamb from a single sheep's cell.

Her creation in a Scottish laboratory immediately stirred visions of a chilling world where humans too could be replicated for far darker purposes.

As her creators admitted cloning of humans could be achieved within two years, Nobel Prize winners joined US President Bill Clinton in calling for strict controls.

Nightmare scenarios of women giving birth to the clones of their dead fathers, or egomaniacs recreating themselves in their own image, were raised. The Pope warned of a threat to the dignity of human life itself.

In America, the cloning of two monkeys brought the new science a tantalising step closer to replicating people.

But the tide has begun to turn. Scientists argue that the cloning technique developed at the Roslin Institute may pave the way to life-saving medical treatments, while politicians have appealed for an end to moral panic.

After the outcry over Dolly, Professor Robert Winston, Britain's leading expert on fertility, makes a provocative argument in favour of cloning.

'Pictures of Dolly, the cloned sheep, are disturbing. It seems such a short step to human cloning. The idea of carbon copies of people naturally causes horror.

'What if Saddam Hussein takes some of his skin cells and has them made into embryos which are then implanted into the wombs of Iraqi women? Other abhorrent notions include trying to replace a dead or dying relative by these techniques.

'It is frightening that human beings are at risk of becoming mere commodities, created at the whim of some mad scientist, or worse still, a totalitarian government. Yet I believe that this sheep clone is a remarkably valuable result of the best British science.

After the outcry over Dolly, Professor Robert Winston, Britain's leading expert on fertility, makes a provocative argument in favour of cloning

---

'The way her birth was reported has obscured the promise this technology offers to mankind, and the value it could have for the welfare of other species inhabiting our planet.

'First it is necessary to consider how she was conceived.

'The nucleus of an adult sheep's cell – in this case the nucleus from the cell of the udder – was inserted into another sheep's egg.

'This egg had been prepared by having its own nucleus removed.

'The resulting embryo was then placed in the womb, where it grew into a lamb.

'Consequently Dolly grew with most of her characteristics derived from the nucleus of the one adult cell.

'The first thing missed in the debate about Dolly is that she is not identical to either of her parents. Although most of her DNA comes from the adult cell nucleus, some of her vital DNA came from the substance of the egg.

'She is less of a "clone" than are identical twins, naturally formed by the spontaneous splitting of an embryo. Identical twins carry

identical DNA from the nucleus and also the egg substance but they are not the same person.

'We are as much a product of nurturing and environment, as we are of our genetic nature.

'A clone of Saddam Hussein would be brought up at a different time and environment from its father. Who knows what gentle and pleasant person might result from a different, loving and supportive environment?

'One of the most important things that could be learned by studying cloning concerns the ageing process.

'Ageing mostly results from changes in the DNA of the egg substance, not the nucleus.

'One intriguing question is: "How old is Dolly?" Is she aged zero – the age of the DNA in her egg substance, or is she adult – the age of the DNA from the nucleus? Cloning research could elucidate many processes which lead to ageing and find ways of limiting their effects.

'There are other important benefits. By transferring a nucleus to another cell, we learn how that cell's subsequent growth is controlled. After transfer, the sheep's nucleus underwent huge changes and its genes were reprogrammed.

'This initiated genes usually only working at the beginning of embryonic life. This control process is not understood but some of these genes, when they go wrong, cause cancer.

'By studying how genes can be reprogrammed we could have a powerful weapon against cancer.

'The nucleus also regulates cell growth. During early development, the cells make all the different tissues which make up a complete body.

'This process of differentiation is poorly understood. It would be a great boon if we could use nuclear transfer to generate new tissues in the laboratory.

'We might make new skin for transplant to the severely burned patient. We could possibly manufacture new blood cells for the young leukaemia victim – such as Sue Harris, who died aged 34 after a long search for a compatible bone marrow donor, and Jaymee Bowen, 11, who became involved in an NHS battle for funding before her tragic death.

By studying how genes can be reprogrammed we could have a powerful weapon against cancer

Hundreds of thousands of people have Parkinson's disease or Alzheimer's and this might be treatable with new nerve cells. None of these techniques needs cloning a person, just specific cells.

'Cloning technology may also be useful in infertility. Many men are unable to produce sperm cells. For them, advances in IVF are useless. Their only chance of a child is adoption or insemination using donor semen. Cloning technology may make it possible for such men to produce a nucleus for transfer with one set of chromosomes effectively just like a sperm cell.

'It was suggested that the sheep cloning procedures could be used to produce "better" farm animals – for example, genetically similar cows all produced by cloning because of their milk yield.

'This is unlikely; indeed, a wrong use of this technology.

'It would result in lack of genetic diversity and protection against resistance to disease.

'If we relied on cows of a similar genetic make-up, and if BSE, for example, is a disease with a genetic predisposition, entire herds could be eliminated.

'Sexual reproduction which allows exchange of genes will always be preferable. But cloning could have real advantages in protecting our environment. It could be used to propagate embryos of endangered species.

'Once such cloned animals had been artificially produced and protected, they could then reproduce themselves by normal mating with others of the same species, thus ensuring protective diversity.

'In Britain the law already prevents cloning humans. Parliament is right to take a considered view and ensure this technology cannot be misused.

'We have time to examine the implications because existing legislation works. Early cloning experiments were done before 1960 and the first pig clone was born in 1988.

'No doctor could consider transferring a clone to the uterus, even if he were tempted.

'There would be no guarantee of a child free of genetic abnormality and the legal liability would be tremendous.

'But apart from pecuniary considerations, it must not be forgotten that doctors and scientists do their work because they want to promote good and relieve suffering.

'Commercial companies are criticised for their involvement with cloning research. But our country earns only 25 per cent of its wealth from manufacturing. In future we shall live increasingly on brains, not brawn.

'Using proper regulation, it would be immoral not to develop this intellectual property with its immense value to our health, our welfare – and our economy.'

© *The Daily Mail*
March, 1997

Cloning presents an opportunity, not a threat

Why shouldn't we clone human beings? It seems likely that scientists will soon find a way to produce a healthy baby that is an exact genetic replica of an existing person. After the cloning of Dolly the sheep, there are still problems with inserting into a new animal genes which have been damaged by the passage of time, but they are almost certain to be solved. More to the point, once human cloning is possible, someone, somewhere is going to do it, even if those problems have not been solved. This means a big dislocation in our moral universe.

So we had better decide what we think about it. Our contribution to this debate is simple: we are all for it. We must not try to shackle the human yearning to find things out. The worst response now would be to be guided by our emotional reaction against scientists dabbling in 'unnatural' experiments. Our starting position is that the research must go on and if, when human cloning becomes possible, it seems that we would learn more by doing it, we see no objection in principle.

Of course, messing about with genes is frightening. But the alternative is to say, 'We don't want to know that', and try to stop the onward rush of curiosity, which could have even more frightening consequences. Take the analogy of splitting the atom. That has made the world a more dangerous place, but would it have been right not to do it? At the time, this was not a choice, because the Allies were in a race against the enemies of democracy and, fortunately for us, the right side won. It might have been better to have split the atom and then chosen not to drop the Bomb, but it could never have been right to tell the scientists to stop.

The choice is not so stark now, but the principle still applies. We could argue that, as it is going to happen anyway, it doesn't matter whether or not human cloning is a good thing. The decision yesterday to allow Diane Blood to be inseminated with her dead husband's sperm in Belgium makes a mockery of the British law on fertility, and the same is likely to happen to the British ban on human cloning.

We could argue that it would be wrong for the Western scientific elite to abdicate its leadership, even assuming it could be persuaded to, because that leadership would then pass to those who are less accountable to rational democratic debate, less answerable to international controls.

But neither argument would answer the fundamental question: would it be right to clone a person? Because if there were a good argument against cloning, there would be a good case for international controls of the kind being urged yesterday by Dagmar Roth-Behrendt, a German Euro-MP. The cause of international regulation is not yet hopeless: no one would describe the controls on world-wide proliferation as perfect, but catastrophe has so far been averted.

The possibility of cloning people is in a different category of scientific advance, in that the product would be a person. This undoubtedly raises several disturbing issues, but these have been clouded by B-movie images of scientists as crazed Dr Frankenstein figures. We need to forget the science-fiction idea of clones as some sort of mass-produced robotic slave, and think instead in terms of identical twins. Identical twins are genetically the same as each other, yet grow into distinct and autonomous individuals. It may seem gross to copy a human being, and it is hard to imagine a woman who would want to bear a clone child. But organ transplants were quite recently regarded as a form of grave-robbing, whereas now it would be ethically unsound not to carry out a transplant if it were possible to do so.

It may seem unfair to the individuals concerned that they should discover their artificial origin and then live their lives as scientific experiments. But Louise Brown, the first test-tube baby, has lived with her (admittedly less dramatic) knowledge, and it is one of the characteristics of living things that they tend not to resent being alive.

Some of the critics of cloning have called for research to be directed instead into finding a cure for cancer or for Aids. This is a piquant misunderstanding, because it is the technology of cloning and genetic manipulation which offers the most promising avenues for doing precisely these things.

That is why, while we applaud the spirit and foresight of our legislators, we do not agree with the ban on human cloning in the 1990 Human Fertilisation and Embryology Act, which was supported by the genetic advisory committee yesterday. The response to scientific discoveries should not be bans but more research, more debate, more involvement by scientists themselves in public argument, and more political controls, including international agreements.

The case against humanity's ability to safeguard its destiny is not made by scientific breakthroughs, but by our collective inability to protect our environment and sustain the ecology of the planet. In the end, cloning and genetic manipulation are more likely to provide the solution to this threat than to add to it.

© *The Independent*
February, 1997

Should we clone animals?

By Dr. Donald M Bruce of the Society, Religion and Technology Project, Church of Scotland

Since 1993, a working group of the Society, Religion and Technology Project (SRT) of the Church of Scotland has been examining ethical issues of genetic engineering. This inter-disciplinary group of experts includes Roslin scientists Dr Ian Wilmut, head of the team who cloned Dolly. The following article by the Director of the SRT project reflects on some of the ethical issues, straight from the sheep's mouth.

Dolly and her applications

Dolly is the most famous sheep in the world. She look much like any other sheep, but she has been cloned from another adult sheep. Scientists at the Roslin Institute in Edinburgh have rewritten the laws of biology. Her announcement in February 1997 led to an unprecedented media circus which caused as much confusion as it shed light. The attention focused mainly on speculations about the possibility, or otherwise, of cloning of humans. In doing so, it missed the much more immediate impact of this work on how we use animals. It is by no means certain this would really lead to flocks of cloned lambs in the field and hills of Scotland, or clinically reproducible cuts of meat on the supermarket shelves. But it does prompt us to ask questions about the way we are using animals with new technology, and the kinds of assumptions we make.

Cloning had already been done to a limited degree by splitting embryos, mostly in cattle, and raised ethical and welfare concerns in the process, But the Roslin work opens up the prospect of a far wider range of applications from adult animal cells. At the moment, there are only a few early results in sheep, and rather little is understood of how it has happened. Different farm animal

species differ somewhat in their embryology. It remains to be seen whether the method would work in any other animal, and without adverse effects. But assuming it could be applied more widely, what are the potential applications in animals?

Since 1986, Roslin have been genetically modifying sheep to produce proteins of therapeutic value in their milk. Successful as this has been so far, the present methods are very hit and miss, using perhaps 100 live animals to get just one right one. The original aim of Dr Wilmut's nuclear transfer work was to find more precise methods by genetic modification, via a cell culture, if a way could be found to grow live animals from the modified cells. Their announcement in July 1997 of the transgenic cloned sheep, Polly, marked the first evidence of this principle. The fact it was a clone was, in a way, a side-effect. PPL Therapeutics, the Edinburgh firm behind the research, say they might clone 5-10 animals like this from a single genetically modified cell line, but then breed them naturally, as 'founders' of a set of lines of genetically modified animals. There would be no advantage in cloning beyond the first point.

But these medical applications tend to be a small scale affair. The amount of animals and the amount of milk is very small compared to conventional meat of bulk milk production. Imagine you are a commercial breeder of cows or pigs, and over many generations you have bred some fine and valuable beasts with highly desirable characteristics. One possible application of Roslin's work could be to clone such animals from the cells of one of them, and sell the cloned animals to 'finishers' – those farmers who simply feed up the animals for slaughter, rather than breed them to produce more stock. Again, the breeder might want to clone a series of promising animals in a breeding programme, in order to test how the same 'genotype' responded to different environmental changes.

Ethics and animal cloning

Should cloning be allowed ethically? To look at this, here are several possible criteria – unnaturalness, diversity, fundamental concerns, animal welfare and commodification:

Is it unnatural?

Many people say that cloning farm animals would be unnatural. Whereas in the plant kingdom cloning is a fairly common phenomenon, there are few animal examples and none in mammals or humans. Should we then respect this biological distinction, or should we celebrate our human capacity to override such limitations? It is hard to argue in an absolute sense that anything is unnatural, when so little remains around us that we might justifiably call natural, and nature itself is in constant motion. Yet many believe some technological inventions are now going too far to remain in tune with what we perceive 'natural' to mean, despite how much we have intervened in nature to date. Is cloning animals a point at which to draw a line?

Would it narrow genetic diversity too far?

This brings us to the question of diversity. One of the fundamental rules of selective breeding is that you must maintain a high enough level of genetic variation. The more you narrow down the genetic 'pool' to a limited number of lines of, say, animals for meat or milk production, the more you run risks of problems of in-breeding. If that is the case with breeding, how much more is it true of cloning, where genetic replicas are involved? This means there are pragmatic limits to how useful cloning would be, but beneath the pragmatics there lies a deeper ethical concern. Does this reflect something fundamental about the nature of things?

Is there a fundamental ethical concern?

This is something for which Christian theology provides some insights. For the Christian, the world around us is God's creation, and one of its most characteristic features is variety. The biblical writers make repeated allusions to it, painting striking pictures of a creation whose very diversity is a cause of praise to its creator. It could be argued that to produce replica humans or animals on demand would be to go against something basic and God-given about the very nature of higher forms of life. Where God evolves a system of boundless possibilities which works by diversification, is it typically human to select out certain functions we think are the best, and replicate them? Deliberate cloning aims at predictability, replication, in order to exercise control, whose centralised, even totalitarian approach, contrasts with God's command to animals and humans to 'be fruitful and multiply'. In the limit this argument would mean that cloning would be absolutely wrong, no matter what it was being used for. This intention runs deep in many people. But there are also questions of scale and intention to consider.

Justifiable used of cloning?

Cloning animals might be acceptable in the limited context of research or, where the main intention was not the clone as such but growing an animal of a known genetic composition, there natural methods would not work. Roslin's work to produce Polly the transgenic cloned sheep would be such a case, where the intention is not primarily to clone, but to find more precise ways of animal genetic engineering. Indeed, producing medically useful proteins in sheep's milk is one the least contentious genetic modifications in animals, since the intervention in the animal is very small for a considerable human benefit. Careful scrutiny would be needed, to see that it was only applied genetic manipulations that would be ethically acceptable, but that is a question we already faced before cloning.

Animal welfare concerns

We also need to be sure about the animal welfare aspects even of limited cloning.

Questions have been raised about the number of failed pregnancies and unusually large progeny which appear to be resulting from Roslin's nuclear transfer experiments to date. While the suffering is not so great as to put a stop to this work, it is clearly necessary to understand the causes and establish whether the problems can be prevented before the methods could be allowed for more general use. If after a reasonable time there seemed little prospect of doing so, however, one would doubt whether it was ethical to go any further. This also points to the serious possibility that any attempt at human cloning could be extremely dangerous for both the clone and the mother, and thus medically unethical, irrespective of wider ethical concerns.

Are there unjustifiable uses of animal cloning?

If an ethical case can be made in favour of Roslin's limited and indirect application of cloning, it is a different matter to apply cloning directly in routine animal production, to accelerate or side-step natural methods. For many, this would be unjustifiable, quite apart from the welfare concerns. What's the problem, you might ask, since we already intervene is nature in selective breeding, and use methods like artificial insemination and embryo transfer? If there was a clear benefit to the farmer to start off with prime stock, to produce the best beef or pork, this might seem to have its attractions. But the answer might lie in a wider question about where we have reached in our human use of animals.

• The above is an extract from *Should we clone animals?*, by Dr. Donald Bruce from the Society, Religion and Technology Project of the Church of Scotland. See page 41 for address details.

Could we now raise the dead?

Nightmare scenario as the cloning debate rages

By David Derbyshire and Michael Harvey

A nightmare scenario of people 'brought back from the dead' emerged last night.

Scientists revealed that freezing played a major role in the creation of Dolly the sheep, the first creature ever to be cloned from an adult mammal.

Researchers said they froze live tissue before using it to create the clone.

The revelation in the scientific journal *Nature* raises a string of science-fiction possibilities.

The technique could be used to replicate babies who die at birth or soon afterwards. Parents whose older children are dying might also be tempted to clone a frozen sample of their tissue, although there would be no point in cases of inherited illnesses such as cystic fibrosis.

Some experts believe people could soon be donating tissue samples to be stored in freezers and turned into clones after their death.

The wave of alarm about genetic engineering followed this week's news about seven-month-old Dolly. Scientists at the Roslin Institute and PPL Therapeutics near Edinburgh produced an exact genetic copy of another sheep by taking a cell from the udder, extracting the genetic information and placing it in an unfertilised egg. The breakthrough has caused concern around the world, invoking images of Nazi 'master race' experiments. President Clinton has already ordered a full inquiry.

As Britain's new advisory body on human genetics met for the first time yesterday, Liberal Democrat MP David Alton called for all experiments involving cloning to be suspended while the ethical problems were properly assessed.

Mr Alton, the leading pro-life campaigner in the Commons, warned that humanity was on the path to disaster. He said: 'We have trivialised human nature and denied natural law.

'We are heading for a twenty-first century which will see the emergence of a genetic underclass of the uninsurable, the unbreedable and the unwanted.'

Science and technology minister Ian Taylor sought to calm public alarm, insisting that 'develop-

> *Some experts believe people could soon be donating tissue samples to be stored in freezers and turned into clones after their death*

ments would be closely monitored'.

He said: 'As long as we keep a close eye on genetics and encourage a full and open debate on the new findings, there is much about which to be optimistic. There is considerable potential for it to enhance the quality of our lives.'

While human cloning is illegal in Britain, fears are growing that the process could already be taking place in other countries, particularly in Eastern Europe and Asia.

There is concern that genetic twins could be cloned for spare organs, or that infertile people desperate for children could clone themselves as a last resort.

Dr Richard Dixon, author of *The Genetic Revolution*, warned that geneticists could soon be able to clone frozen samples of human tissue.

'That means we will be able to reproduce those who pay to put their bodies into deep freeze storage – it is only the method of freezing that is critical.'

In the US, thousands of people have been cryogenically frozen at the point of death in the hope that future medical breakthroughs will find a cure for their illness.

A recent survey found that six per cent of Americans would like to be cloned.

Cloning cannot grant anyone's wish for a new lease of life, however. It will produce a genetically identical person, but there is no way that the new individual can have the original's consciousness, memories or personality.

Last night Mr Taylor emphasised that the Human Fertilisation and Embryology Act expressly forbids the techniques used by the Edinburgh scientists being applied to humans.

He said: 'For those who fear that science fiction will come true they should be clear that a broad range of regulatory controls have been put in place to prevent what is undesirable becoming a reality.'

Mr Taylor said the scientific research should help in the fields of medicine and farming.

As Tory MP Bill Cash called for a Commons select committee to be set up to investigate the issue, the new Human Genetics Advisory Commission met for the first time.

The ten-strong group – nine commissioners and chairman Professor Sir Colin Campbell – will advise the Government on ways to build public confidence in new scientific advances.

Sir Colin, vice chancellor of Nottingham University and a former chairman of the Human Fertilisation and Embryology Authority, said genetics and cloning were top of the agenda.

He said: 'It is going to open wonderful possibilities and the most terrifying possibilities. Science in this country and in every other country will not stop. We cannot stop it. But we will try to control and guide science rather than let scientists impose their solutions on us.'

The composition of the commission has been criticised by pro-life campaigners, who claim it has too many members with a direct financial interest in advancing such research.

A recent survey found that six per cent of Americans would like to be cloned

---

The only true lay member is BBC newsreader Moira Stuart. 'Her role is not to be qualified,' said one official. 'We needed someone the public can relate to.'

The commission will meet again in May.

European Commission President Jacques Santer joined the debate yesterday by asking an advisory team of scientists, lawyers and ethicists to investigate whether the EU should take a stance on cloning.

German newspapers raised the spectre of Nazi eugenics experiments, when scientists tried to create a blond, blue-eyed Aryan master race.

'The cloning of human beings would fit precisely into Adolf Hitler's world view,' said the newspaper *Die Welt*. 'There is no doubt that he would have used this technology intensively.'

The business newspaper *Handelsblatt* said: 'We have crossed a barrier we should have left standing. The birth of Dolly is an event not unlike the first nuclear explosion.'

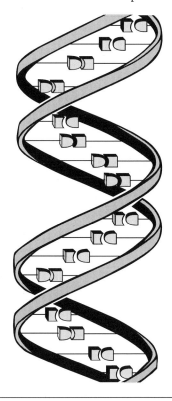

Carbon-copy science

Cloning is possible because every cell in an animal or human body contains a complete set of blueprints for life.

If tissue is removed and frozen quickly enough, this DNA can even be exploited after death.

Dolly was created from a single cell taken from the udder of a live adult ewe.

Scientists removed one nucleus, the part of the cell which contains DNA, and placed it in a 'coma' by soaking it in a chemical bath. This slowed down the nucleus and made it 'forget' it was responsible for producing milk.

The newly programmed nucleus was then injected into an unfertilised egg from another ewe – from which the genetic material had been removed – and placed between two electrodes.

A tiny electric current kicked the embryo into life before it was implanted in a foster mother. A few months later, Dolly was born.

Previously scientists were able to clone sheep only from immature cells found in embryos.

The real breakthrough, published in the science journal *Nature* yesterday, was in persuading the DNA to start its growth programme again from scratch.

The Roslin team say that human cells are far more complicated than sheep cells and years of research are needed before a nucleus taken from a man or woman can be put into a similar 'coma'.

Attempts to use the process on frogs and mice have already failed because it is more difficult to put their cells into the required form of genetic coma.

But judging from the speed of change in recent years, technology that works with human cells may be just a couple of years away.

American scientists have already cloned human embryos in a test-tube by mimicking the way nature creates twins.

Primitive embryos, made of a handful of cells, were split and allowed to grow separately. They survived only a few hours, but the 1993 experiment provoked a bitter row over ethics. © *The Daily Mail February, 1997*

Man or mouse?

Britain's new Human Genetics Advisory Commission met for the first time this week. John Crace looks at the recent developments in genetic engineering and assesses the ethical implications

Last week's announcement that scientists have succeeded for the first time in making a clone – an exact copy – of an adult animal has raised new concerns about the ethics of genetic engineering. Dolly, a Finn Dorset lamb, who is the identical twin of her genetic mother, was created seven months ago at the Roslin Institute in Edinburgh by taking a single cell from its mother's udders and planting it into another sheep's egg from which the genetic material had been removed.

The scientists responsible for Dolly claim that their breakthrough will make a significant contribution to our understanding of the ageing process and could also result in the production of cheaper and more effective medicines.

However, others fear that this advance has brought us nearer to the nightmare scenario depicted in the 1979 film *The Boys from Brazil*, starring Sir Laurence Olivier, where human clones of Adolf Hitler were fashioned.

At present human cloning is prohibited in the UK, but there are many other countries where such laws are not in force. Professor Lord Winston, one of this country's leading IVF (In Vitro Fertilisation) experts, based at the Hammersmith Hospital in west London, believes that no one would dream of making a human clone, pointing to the fact that there is no obvious advantage to be gained and that the transfer of genetic material is inherently risky.

Even so, Dr Patrick Dixon, author of *The Genetic Revolution*, suggests that almost any technique that can be performed on an animal can be reproduced on a human and he, himself, recently received a request from a woman who wanted to create a clone of her dead father. Dixon goes on to say that possible uses of cloning might include people with serious illnesses who want to create the perfect match for transplant surgery, parents who fear losing a child to cot death and film producers who want to recreate dead stars.

Others fear that scientists may produce mutant animals. The British physicist Joseph Rotblat, who won the 1995 Nobel peace prize for his campaign against nuclear weapons, has warned that genetic engineering may lead to the manufacture of new weapons of mass destruction. To guard against this he has called for the establishment of an international ethical committee to control the work of all scientists involved in cloning.

What are genes?

Genes are the basic units that determine the characteristics of every living thing and are passed on from parents to children. We inherit many factors in our genes, from hair colour to our ability to make the necessary enzymes our bodies need to keep us alive.

The process by which we inherit our characteristics depends on structures in our cell nuclei called chromosomes. These are made of long chain-like molecules called deoxyribose nucleic acid (DNA) that carry a genetic code, made up of a series of messages composed of the chemicals adenine, cytosine, guanine and thymine. Every living organism (apart from identical twins) has its own unique code.

Gene therapy

It is estimated that humans have between 50,000 to 100,000 different genes; some of these are linked to particular diseases and conditions. Scientists have now identified 4,000 conditions that are linked to single defects in a person's genetic code. Researchers around the world are currently engaged in 'The Human Genome Project', which aims to identify and define the function of every gene to be found in the human

body. Through this, they hope to locate errant genes, thereby getting a better understanding of every disease that is genetically transmittable and, if possible, find a cure for it. Genetic engineering, whereby the defective gene sequence is cut and remodelled, is one route scientists might take.

In 1993 it was hoped to effect a gene therapy cure for adenoise deaminase (ADA) deficiency, a rare condition which cripples the immune system. However, this treatment has not proved as successful as had been hoped, and despite widespread optimism among geneticists, they do not appear to be any nearer to finding gene cures for the big killers, such as cancer and heart disease.

Predicting disease

At present, genetics can be a reliable predictor of who is likely to develop a particular fatal illness, without the capacity to offer a cure. Many feel that this information has the potential to cause as much harm as good, among the 10 per cent of the population who may be affected. Only last month the Association of Insurance Brokers announced that it would not offer life insurance cover for over £100,000 for those who had a genetic test that predicted a fatal disease, and there are concerns that such tests will promote the idea of eugenics (selective breeding) among prospective parents. Such worries are not mere speculation; three years ago the Chinese government banned all those with 'unhealthy' genes from having babies.

Some also say that people would not be able to cope with the knowledge that they were likely to contract a terminal illness, but geneticists argue that everyone should have the right to know of any flaws in their biological make-up so that they can plan the rest of their lives. Some women who have been told that they are likely to develop breast cancer have opted for a radical mastectomy (surgery to remove the breast) in order to increase their chances of survival.

Animal experiments

Genetic engineering is big business, and many experiments take place on

Scientists grew an ear in a test tube and then transplanted it on to the back of a laboratory mouse that had no immune system to see if it would be rejected

animals. Fruit flies have been produced that have extra eyes on their wings and legs; sheep have been treated to secrete human substances into their milk; two years ago scientists grew an ear in a test tube and then transplanted it on to the back of a laboratory mouse that had no immune system to see if it would be rejected; Harvard University has even patented its own mouse, known as 'oncomouse', which has been genetically manipulated to develop cancer.

Imutran, a Cambridge-based biotechnology firm, have produced a pig that is transgenic (genetically altered to make its immune system compatible with humans), from which they hope to be able to supply donor organs, such as hearts, that are in short supply for transportation. These hearts have already been successfully transplanted into monkeys but, although the Government is believed to have accepted that transplants from animals to humans are in principle ethically acceptable, it has barred any such procedures until more research has been completed.

Those in favour of animal experimentation point to the fact that many of the procedures and drugs we now take for granted, and to which many people owe their lives, were perfected on animals. Some of those against argue that any testing on animals is unacceptable as it is impossible to determine any levels of suffering; when it comes to animal transplantation, others say that the risks of new viruses developing are unquantified and that new diseases may be introduced into humans, as happened when cows, which are natural herbivores, were turned into carnivores by being fed ground-up

sheep protein; through this practice, it is believed that the national herd was infected with BSE (Bovine Spongiform Encephalopathy) and some humans have contracted the human form of the disease, a new strain of Creutzfeld Jacob disease.

Foodstuffs

It is not just animals that are being genetically altered; there is a massive market for producing crops that are larger and more pest and disease resistant. Just how big the industry is can be judged by the fact that in 1991-92 over $6 billion was invested in US biotechnology companies. Already coffee beans have been modified to produce more aroma and less caffeine, genetically modified tomato purée is currently on sale at leading supermarkets, and slow-ripening bananas and pineapples are being developed. At present there are over 2,000 field trials taking place around the world.

The present regulations concerning disclosure of genetic alterations in foodstuffs are likely to prove a minefield for the consumer. The European Government recently announced a proposal to make labelling of all 'genetically modified organisms' (GMOs) compulsory. However, this is only likely to affect products containing living GMOs; items where the GMO has been killed would need no label.

Furthermore, last summer the US began growing GMO varieties of two staple foods, maize and soya, which are used in many different types of foods and drinks. Although these made up a tiny percentage of the overall crop, both the GMO and conventional crops were mixed together. Therefore, many of us might unknowingly and unwillingly already have eaten GMO foods.

The majority of scientists think that GMO foods are safe for human consumption; however, public opinion has recently shifted towards natural organic foods, particularly as a result of the misleading scientific evidence that came out early in the BSE crisis, and many GMO producers are thought to be worried that shoppers will boycott their goods.

© *The Guardian*
March, 1997

Food for our future

A guide to modern biotechnology

We often hear about modern biotechnology and genetically modified foods and food processes. But what does this mean? Where do these foods come from? Are they safe? Why do we need them? This article answers those questions. It is produced by the Food and Drink Federation on behalf of food and drink manufacturers in the UK.

The technology

Throughout history we have relied on natural – biological – processes to make various foods. For example, centuries ago the Egyptians learned how to make wine ferment and how to use yeast to make bread rise. A few hundred years later the Greeks worked out how to graft plants and trees so that they could grow fruit on a larger scale. Scientists refer to these natural processes as 'biotechnology'.

We have also learned how to breed plants and animals with the characteristics we want. This is 'traditional biotechnology'. We know that traits such as the colour of a flower petal or the size of wheat grains are passed on in the genes in the cells of these plants. By selective breeding we can reproduce the characteristics we want and leave out those which are less desirable. However, this can take many years.

With 'modern biotechnology' this process can be more precise and speeded up. We are now able to identify exactly which genes produce which traits. For example, we know which gene makes a tomato go soft when it is ripe. By 'switching off' that gene we can delay the softening of the tomato so that it lasts longer. This is a safe, accurate and reliable way of getting the results we want without the trial and error of selective breeding. This process is called 'genetic modification'.

In the years to come genetically modified foods and food processes could revolutionise our food supply.

The benefits

As the term suggests, modern biotechnology is fairly new so there are only a few products of genetic modification available today. In the coming months and years more will appear in the shops.

Genetic modification will be used for several different reasons in food production. Here are some of the benefits we can expect:

- Crops able to resist diseases from bacteria and viruses and able to defend themselves against attacks by insects.
- Herbicide tolerant crops – this means herbicides can be used to destroy destructive weeds without destroying the crops as well.
- Longer-lasting fruits and vegetables.

- Foods with a higher content of vitamins, mineral or protein or lower in fat – making it easier to choose a healthy diet.
- Crops better able to survive extremes of climate, such as drought or frost.
- Quicker diagnosis of diseases in plants and animals.

Together these benefits will lead to improved quality foods, at lower prices, available to more people throughout the world.

The safeguards

Food manufacturers and retailers want to be absolutely sure that the food they sell is safe. It is also the law that all food sold in this country must be safe to eat. For this reason all foods produced using genetic modification have undergone the closest possible scrutiny to ensure that they are safe, just like other foods.

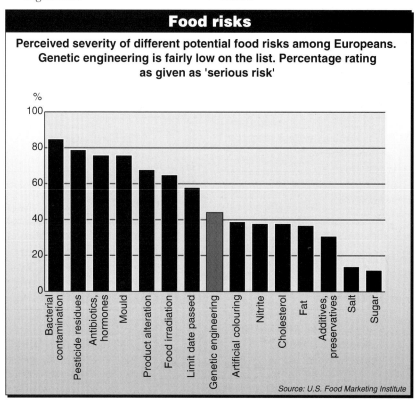

Food risks

Perceived severity of different potential food risks among Europeans. Genetic engineering is fairly low on the list. Percentage rating as given as 'serious risk'

Source: U.S. Food Marketing Institute

Special expert committees have been set up by Government to confirm that these foods are safe. European and UK rules govern every stage of production, from initial laboratory tests and field trials, right through to approval for sale. Similar safeguards exist in the USA where some of the first of these products come from. In fact these foods are some of the most tested foods ever sold.

Even so, some people may want to know which foods have been produced using genetic modification. Individuals – for ethical or religious reasons, or perhaps just from personal choice – may choose not to buy these foods. Manufacturers and retailers are therefore keeping consumers informed about them. They are providing leaflets, Consumer Carelines and, where it is practical and meaningful, informative labelling in-store on the product shelves and/or on the products themselves.

The products

Vegetarian cheese

One of the first products of modern biotechnology is vegetarian cheese. Traditionally when cheese is made, rennet (found in calves' stomachs) is used to turn milk into solid curds and liquid whey. The part of rennet that causes this reaction is an enzyme (which is a protein) called chymosin. Using modern biotechnology, yeast cells have been adapted to produce chymosin which can be used instead of animal rennet to make cheese. This cheese can be eaten by vegetarians.

In this case genetic modification has been applied to the process of making chymosin. Although information about production methods is not usually given on food labels, some retail stores identify this cheese with special labelling. This explains that the cheese is a product of genetic modification and tells consumers that it is suitable for vegetarians.

Tomato puree

Another new product of modern biotechnology is concentrated tomato puree. This is made from the longer-lasting tomatoes mentioned earlier. Because the tomatoes stay firm for longer, fewer are lost during

harvesting and distribution. This reduces waste and saves money. The tomatoes hold less water which means less water is needed to grow them in their dry Californian climate. Because there is less water to remove when turning the tomatoes into paste, energy is also saved during processing. These savings mean the genetically modified puree costs consumers less than other tomato purées.

In this case genetic modification has been applied to the product itself. The consumer benefits from these improvements because the tomato purée costs less than purée made from conventional tomatoes. Some consumers also prefer the taste, texture and appearance of this product. The new purée has therefore been labelled to help consumers choose between the different products.

Soya

Soya beans are high in oil and protein and are a good source of many vitamins and minerals, including vitamin E, folate, calcium, iron, zinc and magnesium. Soya beans are processed to make products such as soya oil, soya lecithin and soya flour which are important ingredients in many everyday foods. Soya beans are also made into animal feed.

Soya beans come mainly from the USA. In 1996 the estimated crop was over 60 million tonnes, covering a vast 60 million acres of land. After harvesting, soya beans from different farms are sold in bulk on the commodity markets; they are also stored and processed in bulk.

Soya beans and modern biotechnology

For years soya bean growers have been looking for better ways to protect their crops from weeds. Modern biotechnology offers a new solution.

One of the herbicides used by soya farmers to kill weeds is glyphosate, sold by the Monsanto company as 'Roundup®'. Roundup® is one of the least toxic herbicides but in the past could only be used before soya crops began to grow, because it would also kill the soya plant. This meant that once the soya plant had emerged from the soil other herbicides which did not kill the soya plant had to be used to kill weeds.

Now a variety of soya plant has been genetically modified so that it is not harmed by Roundup®. The plants are called Roundup Ready™ soya. The advantage is that weeds can now be controlled even after the soya plant has started to grow – and with just one herbicide. It is estimated that around one-third less herbicide overall is used with this system compared with conventional crop management.

The Roundup Ready™ soya beans have been thoroughly evaluated by authorities in the USA, EU and UK and in all countries they have been confirmed safe.

The UK Government's Advisory Committee on Novel Foods and Processes stated that the Roundup Ready™ soya beans ' . . . and products derived from these beans are equivalent to, and as safe for human consumption as beans from other conventional soya bean strains and products derived from them'.

Roundup Ready™ soya beans made up about 15% of the 1997 US harvest. Processed Roundup Ready™ soya beans and their derivatives are in terms of safety, nutritional value and functionality equivalent to their traditional counterparts. Consequently, it is the intention that they will be mixed with and treated just like other soya beans.

Food manufacturers will inform consumers about specific products that contain soya and information can be obtained, for example, via Consumer Carelines and leaflets.

Some of the uses of soya in food

Soya oil is widely used in cooking oils, margarines and spreads. These in turn are used to make a variety of products such as salad dressings, sauces, savoury snacks and bakery products.

Soya flour has many advantages over other flours. It increases the shelf life of many products and improves the colour of pastry crusts. It is used in many foods, including pizzas, noodles, pies, cakes, bread, foods for special dietary needs, meat products and confectionery.

Another product of soya is the emulsifier lecithin; it is often used in ice creams, confectionery, biscuits and margarines.

Soya sauce, made from fermented soya beans, is famous for its use in oriental cooking.

Other foods made from soya include dairy alternatives to milk, yoghurt and cheese and traditional soya alternatives such as tofu, tempeh and miso.

Maize

Another crop important to our food supply is maize, known to Americans as corn. It is one of the world's biggest crops, with a yearly harvest of more than 560 million tonnes.

The majority of maize is used in animal feed and the rest is used for human food. One particular variety is sweet corn which we eat as a vegetable. Two types of maize are used in UK food processing: 'hard' (flint) and 'soft' (dent). The first of these is mainly used in products such as breakfast cereals and comes from South America. The second is usually processed into corn oil, cornflour, starches and glucose syrups which in turn are used in a wide range of every-day foods. Snack foods contain either type, depending on the product's characteristics, with Europe and South America being the major sources of supply. Popcorn is a specific flint variety grown mainly in the USA.

Maize is primarily grown in the USA. Little is exported to Europe as it is self-sufficient in dent maize, which is mainly grown in France and Spain.

Like all crops, maize is exposed to damage from pests. The corn borer alone typically destroys 5-7% of each year's crop. To overcome this problem a number of companies are developing varieties of maize which have been genetically modified so that they are resistant to this pest.

Before these varieties of maize can be grown, or imported and sold unprocessed for use as animal feed, in the UK or any other Member State, an EU marketing consent must be obtained. A number of Member States, including the UK, have identified concerns with the first of these modified varieties which is currently being grown in the USA. The UK concerns relate to the presence of a gene which confers resistance to the antibiotic ampicillin and which could theoretically transfer to bacteria in the intestines of animals fed the unprocessed maize. This might present a risk to animals, and perhaps humans, from bacteria resistant to this antibiotic. The EU examined this issue and, on 18 December 1996, authorised this particular variety. Other varieties of genetically modified maize are being developed and submitted for approval.

The UK Government's Advisory Committee on Novel Foods and Processes has confirmed that the particular variety being grown in the USA is safe when processed for use in human food. It is satisfied that the maize does not differ from its conventional counterpart and that the modified genes in the plant are destroyed during processing.

© foodfuture
November 1997

Store chief's fears over designer veg

Genetic engineering of foods is 'messing about with the building blocks of life', the head of a store chain warned last night.

Malcolm Walker, chief executive of the frozen food company Iceland, admitted he was frightened by what people are now being asked to eat.

'We have sufficient evidence to show that nature fights back – salmonella, listeria, BSE,' he added. He cited the example of BSE, or mad cow disease. 'So-called experts allowed dead sheep to be eaten by herbivores and we were used as human guinea-pigs. Had the commonsense view of the normal consumers been sought, regardless of scientific evidence, it would not have happened.'

Mr Walker said the introduction and lack of labelling of certain genetically modified vegetables, including soya beans, was unacceptable. Americans had mixed the beans unlabelled with ordinary soya – present in everything from chocolate to baby foods – and put the resulting product into world-wide distribution.

'The American public seem at ease with this . . . I for one find it frightening. With genetically modified foods, we have reached the thin end of the wedge. We are messing with the building blocks of life and it's scary.

'We are playing games with nature and unless we make a stand now, the situation could spiral out of control. It is totally unacceptable that American companies should dictate to us in this way.'

Mr Walker, a long-term member of the environmental group Greenpeace, praised its work.

'I support Greenpeace, tactics and all,' he said. 'From a corporate view, they can be extremely irritating, very costly and uncompromisingly demanding but I can't have it both ways.

'Greenpeace has a job to do and I admire its guts.'

© The Daily Mail

The mutant plants that grew into bee killers

By David Derbyshire

Grass could soon be used to wipe out destructive caterpillars and greenfly. Scientists have found that the odour from some types of grass not only repels pests but also attracts wasps that kill them. Now some could be used as a natural pesticide against bugs in Britain.

The breakthrough, reported in today's *Nature*, came after researchers discovered the odour from African molasses grass attracted the parasitic wasps. Trials in Kenya showed that without molasses grass nearby up to 80 per cent of a maize field was wiped out by pests. But when the grass was planted only five per cent was destroyed.

Molasses does not grow in Britain so scientists are now looking for similar grasses to do the same job.

Plants which have been genetically engineered to ward off pests may be killing bees as well, scientists have warned.

A disturbing study has found that the natural pesticides produced by modified strains of rape seed shorten the life of bees and confuse their sense of smell.

The discovery could force scientists to think again about how they tamper with plant DNA.

Scientists have altered the genetic blueprint of dozens of species, from tomatoes to soya beans, in the race to find longer-lasting, tastier and pest-resistant food.

The altered rape seed was given an extra gene found naturally in some plants which produces a chemical harmless to humans but deadly to pests. The extra protein – known as a protease inhibitor – messes up the digestive system of beetles and caterpillars. Unable to feed on the rape seed's leaves and stalks, the pests die of starvation.

But scientists discovered that bees, exposed to the destructive chemical through pollen and nectar, are also wiped out, *New Scientist* magazine reports today.

> **Scientists have altered the genetic blueprint of dozens of species, . . . in the race to find longer-lasting, tastier and pest-resistant food**

'Rape seed is particularly important to bees,' said Dr Minh-HaPham-Delegue of the Laboratory of Comparative Invertebrate Neurobiology in France.

'The plants do not depend strictly on bees to pollinate them, but it is the first plant to bloom in large quantities in the spring. Bees harvest a lot of nectar from them.'

Pollen and nectar from rape seed contain only low levels of the chemicals. But scientists fear they could build up to harmful concentrations in honey eaten in the hive.

The researchers studied the effects of the chemicals by feeding them to laboratory bees in a sugar solution. After three months, the insects died up to 15 days earlier than those fed on normal sugar. After just two weeks, bees had trouble distinguishing between different flowers. Now that scientists know the rape seed protein kills bees, the next step is to establish how much of it actually gets back to the hive.

Genetic engineering

Information from Compassion in World Farming (CIWF)

Introduction

Genetic engineering is the taking of genes from one species of plant or animal and inserting them into a completely different species (also altered genes from the same animal). This does not happen in nature except in very rare circumstances. Even when animals of different species mate, their young grow up to be sterile and cannot breed, i.e. horses and donkeys can mate to produce mules, but two mules cannot produce further mule offspring.

What are genes?

Genes are chemical messengers made from a complex chemical called DNA. Genes carry the information about how we look, some of our behaviour patterns and other characteristics. Genes are passed on through generations. You, for example, will have inherited your particular eye or hair colour from your parents or grandparents. Your genes will also be an important factor in determining how tall and big you will grow and so on.

How are the genes transferred from one species to another?

A female animal's egg which has already been fertilised by a male sperm is taken from the oviduct (tube leading from ovary to womb where fertilisation usually occurs) and is injected with the new gene from a different species (or an altered gene from the same species). This process is called micro-injection; the egg is very small and the whole process is done under the microscope using very tiny equipment. The egg is then put into the womb of a foster mother who will give birth to a *transgenic* animal (an animal that has been given a gene from another animal). Transferring this egg is done by an often painful process called embryo transfer.

Why do scientists want to produce transgenic animals?

These are the main reasons:

- To increase the amount of milk, meat etc. produced by an animal. Scientists aim to make animals grow faster and produce less fatty meat.

- To make farm animals resistant to diseases which are usually common in intensive farming systems.

- To produce animals which are highly likely to develop a particular disease – for example, cancer.

- To produce animals which make proteins in their milk/blood for pharmaceutical production.

- Also to produce animals whose organs might be used in human transplant operations.

Where were the first transgenic animals produced?

The first transgenic mammal was a mouse and this was produced in 1981. The first transgenic farm animals were sheep and pigs produced in 1985.

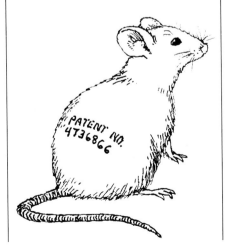

How are animal growth rates speeded up?

Growth rates can be speeded up in animals like pigs by inserting extra growth hormone genes, either more of the pig hormone gene, or cow or human growth hormone gene. The transgenic pig should grow more quickly and produce less fatty meat. These characteristics should also be passed on to the piglets. However, there have been some terrible failures. In the USA, pigs that were born with an extra bovine growth hormone gene suffered dreadfully from arthritis, were almost blind and could not produce piglets.

How is genetic engineering affecting cows?

Dairy cows can also be given growth hormone genes so that they will produce more milk. One researcher has already predicted much larger cows producing twice as much milk as today's high-yielding cow. Scientists are also trying to alter the nature of the milk – e.g. to make it more like human milk or more suitable for making cheese or long-life milk straight from the cow etc.

What about genetically engineered poultry?

Poultry are being engineered to produce more meat and eggs. A transgenic chicken with a cow growth hormone gene has been developed.

Modern broiler chickens already suffer because they grow so quickly – imagine the welfare problems of the transgenic chicken with added cow growth hormone.

Are these experiments successful?

Frequently not. Genetically engineered lambs developed a fatal diabetic condition. Calves have grown too big to be born naturally, and of course often the gene doesn't get passed on and lots of 'failures' are born. Scientists are trying to get these failures sold as ordinary meat.

Will genetic engineering protect animals from disease?

Attempts are being made to genetically engineer farm animals to make them resistant to disease but as yet there are no successful examples. Chickens which were thought to have been made resistant were instead made to have the disease.

What is animal 'pharming'?

Experiments are being carried out to produce a protein called AAT (which is used to treat the lung disease emphysema) in the milk of sheep. Although the protein has been produced it has not yet been shown to be effective or safe. This means there will be several years of tests to see if the protein will be useful against emphysema. Before the scientists start testing their new techniques on large animals like sheep, they 'try

out' their ideas on many small animals such as mice and rabbits.

Is meat etc. from genetically engineered animals on sale?

Not yet. But genetically engineered pigs may soon be on sale in Australia. CIWF believes that if such meat is sold it should be clearly labelled (although we believe it should not be sold in the first place).

What does CIWF say?

CIWF believes that the production of transgenic farm animals cannot be done without causing suffering to those animals and to their parents and surrogate parents. We would therefore like to see an end to the genetic engineering of farm animals. In a recent EC poll only 14% of the public supported genetic engineering when animal suffering was involved, even to develop life-saving drugs.

What you can do

1 If you are interested in campaigning for the welfare of farm animals join CIWF's Young

Supporters Group. It's FREE! Send us your full name, address and date of birth and we'll enrol you. You will then receive our colour newsletter *FarmWatch* and be kept up to date with our campaigns.

2 Tell your friends about the information in this article and get them to join CIWF's Young Supporters Group too.

3 Many people do not fully understand the issues of genetic engineering. Try to get them discussed at your school or youth group.

Write to your MP regarding your concerns about genetic engineering and urge him or her to write to the Agriculture Minister to ban the production of transgenic farm animals. He/she can be contacted c/o The House of Commons, London SW1A 0AA.

Help us to help farm animals. Together we can help make a difference to their lives.

© Compassion in World Farming Trust (CIWF)

Why the gene green grass of home stays eternally emerald

It's every gardener and grounds-man's dream – grass that stays green all summer with no need for watering.

Thanks to some cunning genetic engineering, the dream is on the verge of reality, with consequences likely to change the face of Britain.

The new species of super-grass, guaranteed to stay lush all year round, will see off brown baselines at Wimbledon and tan turf at Lord's – while golf courses, motorway verges and garden lawns will also keep their colour. 'It is difficult to over-emphasise its impact because it will utterly revolutionise garden lawns, golf courses and agricultural grassland,' said Roger Saunders of British Seed Houses, the company planning to launch the grass in 2000.

'It will remain green in the win-

By David Derbyshire, Science Correspondent

ter and throughout a drought. And it won't need to be watered which will preserve valuable resources.'

The new strain is related to a mutant species of naturally-growing meadow grass first spotted in the 1960s.

Despite years of research, it was only a few years ago that biologists discovered which gene allowed the mutant to keep its colour.

That mutant gene, which suppresses the enzyme that attacks the green pigment in leaves, has been spliced with perennial rye grass, the hardy species used for soccer pitches and back gardens.

Fields of the new grass are being exposed to the elements at the Institute of Grassland and Environmental Research in Aberystwyth, mid-Wales.

Apart from colour, it has the same qualities as normal varieties, said Mr Saunders.

Dr Sarah Ball, of the Royal Horticultural Society, said: 'We look forward to the day when gardens and lawns will look good without having to use precious water resources.'

Despite popular myth, grass does not die when it loses its colour in droughts, it is simply resting. The new version will also rest in extreme weather, but will not turn yellow or brown.

© The Daily Mail February, 1997

Food and biotechnology

Information from _foodfuture_, an initiative of the Food and Drink Federation

Is it safe?

Opponents of genetic modification argue that we do not know enough about the science and that altering genes could lead to unforeseen problems for future generations.

Against that it is argued that strict controls are in place and each modified product is very thoroughly assessed for any difference from its conventional counterpart. In addition, since only the specific genes for a trait are identified and copied, the technology is far more precise than the trial and error approach of traditional plant and animal breeding.

What laws exist?

In the UK, the Food Safety Act requires that ALL food must be fit for consumption, i.e., must not be injurious to health, be unfit or contaminated. An additional set of safeguards controls the use of genetic modification in foods or food ingredients. These foods are assessed by a number of committees of independent experts, some of which include consumer representatives:

- The Advisory Committee on Novel Foods and Processes (ACNFP)
- The Committee on Toxicity of Chemicals in Food, Consumer Products and the Environment (COT)
- The Food Advisory Committee (FAC)

The Annual Reports of these Committees are a useful starting-point for those who wish to check if, and how, issues of concern are being addressed.

At European level, the Novel Foods Regulation on Novel Foods and Food Ingredients has been adopted, after 4½ years of discussion. It came into force on 15 May 1997. It will harmonise procedures for the

foodfuture

approval of all novel foods, including those produced using modern biotechnology. This legislation formalises the UK's previous voluntary procedures which provided a blue print for the European Scheme.

What about labelling?

The requirement for labelling are set out in the EU Regulations on Novel Foods and Novel Food Ingredients which were adopted in May 1997. Voluntary guidelines have also been drawn up by the food industry and major retailers to amplify and help implement these rules.

As a result of these developments, whenever genetic modification is used to make a product which is 'no longer equivalent' to its conventional counterparts, it would be labelled. Situations where this would apply include the following:

- The food or food ingredient differs from an equivalent food or food ingredient such as in its composition, nutritional value or intended use.
- These could be implications for health for certain sections of the population; for example, for those suffering from food allergies.
- There may be ethical concerns.
- As far as practicable, where there is a genetically modified organism present.

Practical considerations

These guidelines encompass the most significant applications of genetic applications of genetic modification. However, many consumers do not believe they go far enough and want all products of the technology to be labelled. Against this the practicalities have to be considered. Genetically modified commodity crops are one example. They are sold in vast quantities on the international markets. To segregate them so that they could be labelled would be extremely difficult and expensive as it would require separate production and handling facilities at every stage of the supply chain.

Would it be useful and meaningful to the consumer to provide comprehensive information on the label about every single ingredient in a food is also available via customer care telephone lines and the many consumer leaflets provided by the industry and major retailers.

Clearly, much more debate is needed before these important issues can be resolved.

What about the environment?

A main concern is that copy genes incorporated into a plant could 'escape' and transfer to another species with unwanted consequences. For example, it is argued that herbicide-resistant crops could cross-pollinate with weeds and so become herbicide-resistant themselves. Thus 'superweeds' could be created.

Some consumers and farmers are also concerned that making crops herbicide-resistant might lead to an increase in herbicide use, as the crops could withstand higher doses.

Supporters of biotechnology argue that stringent rules exist to safeguard against these possibilities and that the development of genetically modified plants will mean a decrease in the use of environmentally unfriendly herbicides.

What laws exist?
UK regulations (in addition to the EU Novel Foods Regulation) which implement European Directives, control laboratory experiments, field trials and commercial use:
- The Genetically Modified Organisms (Contained Use) Regulations 1992
- The Genetically Modified Organisms (Deliberate Release) Regulations 1992

In the UK, the regulatory bodies are the Health and Safety Executive and the Department of the Environment. The latter is advised by the Advisory Committee for Releases to the Environment (ACRE) which is responsible for assessing genetically modified organisms into the environment in the UK.

Extensive risk assessment trials are also being carried out in various countries to assess the environmental impact of releasing genetically modified plants. Again, the Annual Reports of these bodies are a useful starting-point for those who wish to check if, and how, issues of concern are being addressed. As with the subject of safety, it will remain important that consumer groups continue to be informed and to play a part in the decision-making process.

Who should own the rights?
Patent laws protect inventions for a fixed number of years. During this period no one else can copy or use the invention without permission, which usually has to be paid for. Should patent protection extend to genetic modification of foods?

The case for:
- Patent protection enables investors to recoup their considerable investments in research and development; without it, far less research funding would be available.
- A prerequisite of patent protection is that the details of the patent must be published. Without patent protection, more inventions would be kept secret, which would slow up the development of the science.

The case against:
- Genes are not 'inventions' and therefore should not be subject to patent rights. Life should not be patentable.
- It is wrong that our food supplies could be controlled by the few who can afford the development costs. Food should be available to all.
- Patents tend to benefit the developed countries exclusively; it is important that developing countries have access to these important new technologies.

These conflicting viewpoints have been debated at length at EU level where a directive on biotechnology patents is being agreed. The directive grants patent protection for genes and genetically engineered plants and animals provided an <u>invention</u> has been made. The mere <u>discovery</u> of the function of a specific gene cannot be patented. In the case of patents on animals, a 'morality clause' requires patent examiners to weigh up the level of suffering to the animal against the benefit to human or veterinary medicine.

Will developing countries benefit?
The case for:
- Crops could be especially adapted to the diverse farming conditions and practices, and offer greater nutritional value and a higher income.
- Energy producing crops could also save natural resources and so conserve the environment.

The case against
- Genetically modified products could reduce the developed countries' reliance on crops from developing countries. This could result in loss of trade and serious economic damage.
- Other doubt whether developing countries will actually receive the benefits.

These issues raise important political, ethical and trade questions which are not unique to modern biotechnology. They must be resolved at Government and Intergovernmental level to make sure that everyone benefits from the new technology.

Is it ethical?
Most people find the idea of genetically modifying plants acceptable, although some people disagree with all genetic modification on the grounds that we should not tamper with nature.

There is also concern about the possibility of transferring genes of an animal or human origin to other animal species and plants.

However, the current consensus among scientists it that whilst the use of human copy genes in food production is theoretically possible, in practice it is very unlikely to be pursued. The use of animal copy genes in plants is more likely, but still very much dependent on consumer acceptance.

The Polkinghorne Committee
The UK Government set up a committee to consider these points, chaired by the Reverend Dr John Polkinghorne. It found that:
- Most Christian and Jewish groups in general find modification acceptable;
- Muslims, Sikhs and Hindus have ethical objections to consuming organisms containing copy genes from animals which are the subject of dietary restrictions for their religion;
- Strict vegetarians would object to incorporating copy genes of animal origin in a plant.

The Committee recommended that, should this happen, clear labelling would be required to allow these groups to make an informed choice.

Conclusion
Some of the concerns outlined in this article can be resolved by making more facts available to consumers. Others are more a matter of opinion and need to be discussed further.

The biotechnology debate, involving governments, scientists, industry and consumer groups, has already begun. Further wide-ranging and open discussions must continue so that all concerns can be properly addressed. Only then can we all benefit from the massive potential of the new technology.

© foodfuture
November, 1997

Why be concerned?

Information from the Green Alliance

Genes inserted into micro-organisms, plants and animals, that could not have got there by conventional breeding, will over time be spread to other organisms.

- Genetic manipulation technologies enable scientists to cross the barriers in nature that normally mean that only closely related varieties or species can interbreed.

   Genes from viruses have been put into plants, for instance, putting part of a virus into crops such as potatoes and beet to give resistance to that virus[1]. Genes from animals have been put in viruses, for instance, putting scorpion toxin genes into a virus that attacks caterpillars to make it a more effective pesticide[2]. Genes from bacteria are regularly put into plants, to confer traits such as disease resistance and herbicide resistance.

- The extent to which introduced genes will transfer to near relatives, or other organisms, is not always clear.

   Ecologists have identified at least 10 crops plants which have been genetically modified and are capable of forming 'persistent feral populations', in other words, plants survive on roadsides and other land long after the original crop has been grown in a field. The existence of these feral populations means that there is a continual potential source of introduced genes, which may then transfer to wild relatives through hybridisation. Of these 10 crops at least six have high rates of hybridisation with particular wild relatives, including sugar beet, cabbage, carrot and colver.[3]

   A recent application by Plant Genetic Systems to market a herbicide-resistant rape in the EU said in the risk of assessment that 'the opportunity for *Bassica rapa* and

Brassica juncea to act as a bridge for gene transfer from *Brassica napus* (rape) to its wild relatives cannot be totally excluded . . . hard data on likelihood under natural conditions are lacking. The frequency of such exchange is deemed to be very low.'[4] However, Greenpeace submitted in response to the PGS proposal, 'Although the estimated frequency of a harmful event, such as the transfer of the herbicide gene to weedy relative, is low, the potential scale of the release is enormous. Therefore rare events will occur. Marketing applications must be viewed in a very different light to field trials.'[5]

- Such spread could mean 'genetic contamination' of the gene pools of some native plants and animals – in other words, naturally occurring genes could be replaced by introduced ones, leading to a reduction in biological diversity.

Responsibility for action lies with:
- Those who shape research agendas, including industry, to put emphasis on understanding of gene transfer from crops, and the effects of introduced traits in natural population, including the effects on genetic diversity.
- Risk assessment within regulatory systems to take into account the possibility of genetic contamination.

Regulation of release in the UK
Release of genetically modified organisms (GMOs) in the UK is regulated by the Department of the Environment, using laws made in response to an EC Directive.[6] Anyone proposing to make a release, whether as an experiment or as a product that will be put on the market, must apply to the DOE for a consent. The Advisory Committee on Release to the Environment (ACRE) advises the DOE on the granting of consents and on the future development of the regulatory system. Members of ACRE are people with relevant scientific knowledge, and some represent specific interests such as industry and workers. Julie Hill, the Director of the Green Alliance, is a member of ACRE as an independent environmentalist. The majority of interest groups, including environmental organisations and companies, agree that a specific regulatory regime of this kind is needed to provide public reassurance that the possible risks of GMOs are being considered.

Who determines research agendas?
The European Commission, the Department of the Environment, the Ministry of Agriculture, Fisheries and Food, the Biotechnology and Biological Sciences Research Council and the Natural Environ-ment Research Council all fund scientific research projects that have relevance to the environmental impacts of GMOs. Research funded by Government departments is increasingly directed towards informing or validating Government policy, and less towards so-called 'strategic research', i.e. research looking at longer-term implications. Consultation on the specific projects that should receive support tends to be within or between departments and

does not involve outside interests such as environmental and consumer groups, although some departments do publish an account of their overall aims for research. Research funded by research councils is supposed to be subjected to greater public consultation, according to the recent Government White Paper 'Realising our Potential'. At the end of the process, the Department of the Environment has a policy of publishing the results of the GMO research it supports, and the results of research carried out under the Ministry of Agriculture's Biotechnology Programme are available on request.

The majority of research on GMOs is funded by industry, and a proportion of this research will be related to evaluating environmental impacts. Some companies are considering discussing their research agendas with outside commentators such as environmental groups.

We do not know enough about ecological interactions to be able to accurately predict what the long-term consequences will be of the presence of these introduced genes in the environment.

- Ecological systems are extremely complex.

'Predicting how organisms might behave in a particular habitat is extremely difficult. Nevertheless, ecological insight provides the only basis to explore the potential impact of . . . GMOs that might persist in the unconfined environment. Such insight can never be absolutely precise given the great complexity of ecosystems.'

From the summing up of a major European conference on the long-term impacts of the release of GMOs[7]

- It is difficult to predict the characteristics that will turn a plant into a 'weed'.

Professor Mark Williamson is one of the UK's leading ecologists and a former member of the Advisory Committee on Release to the Environment. These extracts are from two of his scientific papers:

'. . . *the characters responsible for critical ecological behaviour are still obscure. Small genetic changes can cause large ecological changes.*'[8]

'*Some companies wish to change the protein content of the seed of oil-seed rape. This plant is already a minor weed, and it may hybridise with other brassicas . . . Why is oil-seed rape not a worse weed? Why does it not establish more widely? The answers to these questions are not known. Changing the seed proteins in the way proposed could possibly affect the rate of attack (by natural enemies). Will this simple molecular change affect the ecology of feral populations? Will it spread to other brassicas (wild relatives)? These are difficult questions, so it is not surprising the companies try to avoid them. There is no way either a priori or from our present knowledge that they can be answered with any certainty.*'[9]

- There is a very little previous history of measuring the impact of introduced genes.

'. . . *ecologists can best contribute to the debate about the ecological risks of genetically modified crops by attempting to understand the dynamics of these traits in natural populations . . .*'

From a paper by A.F. Raybould and A.J. Gray[10]

- Once an organism becomes a pest it could be eradicated. A living, replicating organism could be as much of a problem as a persistent chemical pollutant, and furthermore can no longer be stopped 'at source'.

Responsibility for action lies with:

- Research agendas to put more emphasis on studying ecosystems and population dynamics, as well as the specific risks posed by GMOs.

- Risk assessment within regulatory systems to take into account the areas of uncertainty, in accordance with the 'precautionary principle'.

Sources:
1 Plant Breeding International experiment to look at virus resistance in potatoes by adding genes from potato virus X and Y. ACRE reference 93/RS/1 filed 01.02.93
2 National Environment Council Institute of Virology series of experiments to look at the effects of adding a scorpion toxin gene to the virus *Autographica californica* NPV, a baculovirus. Department of the Environment references 93/R3/2 filed 25.06.93 and 94/R3/4 filed 17.02.94
3 Raybould, A.F. and Gray, A.J. 1993. 'The Impact of Genetically Modified Crops of Wild Species in the United Kingdom' Proceedings of meeting in Neuchatel, 1993
4 'A new hybridization system in oilseed rape' (also modified for herbicide tolerance) Plant Genetic Systems. ACRE reference 94/M1/1 filed 01.03.94, pp 277 and 284
5 Greenpeace UK letter to ACRE dated 11.04.94, page 1
6 EC Directive 90/220 is implemented in the UK by part VI of the Environment Protection Act 1990, and under that Act by the Genetically Modified Organisms (Deliberate Release) Regulation 1993
7 Concluding remarks by Dr R. Harrington, General Rapporteur for the Council of Europe's Pan-European conference on the potential long-term impacts of the release of genetically modified organisms, Strasbourg, 1993, Proceedings pp. 237-238
8 Williamson, M. 1993. 'Invaders, weeds and risk from genetically manipulated organisms' *Experentia*, 49: 219
9 Williamson, M. 1992. 'Environmental risks from the release of genetically modified organisms (GMOs) – the need for molecular ecology' *Molecular Ecology* 1: 4
10 Raybould, A.F. and Gray, A.J. 1993. 'Genetically modified crops and hybridization with wild relatives: a UK perspective.' *Journal of Applied Ecology*, 30: 204

- The above is an extract from *Why are environmental groups concerned about release of genetically modified organisms into the environment?*, produced by the Green Alliance. See page 41 for address details.

© *The Green Alliance January, 1997*

Will the gene genies change the way you farm?

Should scientists be dabbling in genetics? The public is being asked to give their opinion. National Farmers Union (NFU) food science adviser Vernon Barber looks at what this may mean for farmers

When 'Dolly' the cloned sheep was first led out of her pen into the glare of the spotlight earlier this year, she was greeted with amazement around the world.

Here, at last, was evidence that scientists could play God, some of the headlines claimed. Others welcomed her arrival as the way forward for scientific research, saying that the technology which had created her could help feed the starving and cure the sick.

That technology was genetic engineering, something that the agriculture industry has been embracing for some time in an attempt to increase production efficiency and enhance marketability of its food products. In the US and Canada this year alone, between 10 and 12 million hectares of genetically modified (GM) crops will have been planted, most commonly Monsanto's Roundup Ready Soya and Novartis' Bt maize, both developed to reduce herbicide or pesticide use.

Although there are currently no commercial quantities of GM crops being grown in the UK, there are a large number of test plots. The most extensive programme is that of the Familiarization and Acceptance of Crops with Transgenic Technology project, set up in six countries: Belgium, France, Denmark, Germany, Sweden and the UK. Sixty-nine plots were planted this year with a variety of oilseed rape which has been genetically modified to be tolerant of the herbicide glufosinate.

In the livestock sector, the biotechnology company PPL Therapeutics has clinical trials in progress of the protein a1-antitrypsin, which is purified from the milk of a herd of GM sheep and is being tested as a treatment for human cystic fibrosis.

On the retail side, a number of imported food products developed using GM organisms have now been on sale in the UK for several years now, such as:

- tomato purée made from the Flavr Savr tomato, which used gene technology to delay ripening in order to reduce bruising of the fruit after harvest.
- Vegetarian cheese made with the assistance of chymosin, an enzyme made from GM micro-organisms. This replaces rennet derived from the stomach linings of calves.

Of all these developments, however, it was Dolly that really caught the public's attention. The horrified reaction provoked by her arrival alarmed European legislators and led to President Clinton demanding a full report on the implications of gene technology. In July this year, the British public was asked to give their views for the first time on the growing of GM crops on farms in this country.

In launching the consultation, Food Industry Minister Lord Donoughue said that the Government was yet to take a view either way on the issue of GM organisms.

Amount heard or read about biotechnology

Awareness of biotechnology in the United States appears to be waning. Elsewhere in the world, Northern Europe and Japan appear to be best informed.

Source: Food Marketing Institute

'The new strain of crops could improve the yield for farmers and may result in the use of less chemicals on our fields, benefiting the public,' he said. 'But there could be implications for weed control of the farm and we need a proper debate before these crops come in.'

The NFU has been closely involved in the debate over the use of GM organisms for some time. Its Biotechnology Working Party was established in 1995 to prepare a detailed report to help the NFU Council develop a formal policy. That policy stated that, if used responsibly, biotechnology could have significant benefits for the agriculture industry, such as:

- Helping increase production efficiency.
- Enhancing the marketability of existing products.
- Presenting new market opportunities.
- Improving animal health and welfare.
- Benefiting the environment.
- Assisting underdeveloped and developing countries.

Some specific concerns were identified, most notably relating to the approval of GM organisms containing certain antibiotic resistant marker genes; these were felt to be undesirable and unnecessary. The NFU also felt that there was a need for GM organisms to be officially monitored post-release so that any potential problems could be identified at an early stage.

Since the development of that policy, the NFU has augmented its position by calling for the segregation of imports containing GM organisms so that product labelling could help consumers exercise freedom of choice. This latter point is extremely important to the NFU and has become central to its policy. Lord Donoughue reiterated this same consumer concern back in July when he called for EU-wide rules to force manufacturers into labelling all foods containing GM ingredients.

The unease felt by consumers is hardly surprising taken in light of the BSE crisis. A raft of surveys of consumer attitudes confirm this unease and has led organisations such as Greenpeace and the Soil

Association to publicly oppose the use and sale of foods derived from GM processes.

The European regulations on Novel Foods and Novel Food Ingredients, which came into force in May this year, were expected to calm consumer concerns. Unfortunately they haven't, as foods only have to be specifically labelled if they are substantially different from ones already in existence. Foods containing GM soya and maize are therefore not covered.

The European Commission has recently decided upon its own rules and, from 1 November, all products containing GM material must be clearly labelled. So, too, must products which may contain such material. There is also provision in the rules for voluntary labelling of foods which contain *no* GM organisms. These rules apply retrospectively to any GM products already approved for use in the EU, such as GM soya and maize.

This latter point should help in any cases where retailers require farmers and growers to state whether their products contain any GM material. They will allow producers, for example, to determine the GMO content of animal feedstuffs should they need to do so to meet any farm assurance contract requirements.

NFU action on GM foods

- NFU, UKASTA and the British Society of Plant Breeders have developed two codes of practice encouraging producers to

segregate GM crops on their farms. This will facilitate clear labelling, the codes state, and prevent consumer confusion.
- The NFU has made successful representations to protect farmers' rights on the proposed EC Biotechnology Patenting Directive.
- Staff and officials are in regular contact with consumer groups to keep abreast of their concerns.
- NFU is keeping farmers and growers fully up to speed with the GMO debate and its clear policy on all issues concerning biotechnology.
- Meetings have been held with retailers under the auspices of the Institute of Grocery Distribution concerning the drafting of voluntary guidelines for the labelling of GM food products.

North American farmers win case against segregation of GM crops

It is estimated the soya is included as an ingredient in up to 60% of processed foods, so the decision to plant so many million of hectares of GM crops in North America last year led to considerable consumer concern.

For a variety of reasons, some consumers simply say that they do not wish to eat foods containing GM material. The only way of enabling these people to exercise informed choice is by segregating conventional crops from those developed from GM material. Producers opposed segregation, claiming that the costs of complying with it would make the growing of GM crops uneconomic. The US Government has so far supported their stance.

Bt maize has caused additional concern because of the presence of an antibiotic-resistant marker gene. This might be transferable to microorganisms in the digestive system of farm animals, and – possibly – to humans as well. It is unlikely, however, that processed maize will contain viable genetic material, although some matter is very stable and fragments can survive certain processing procedures.

© NFU Magazine Autumn 1997

Ethical, safety and other questions

Information from the Biotechnology and Biological Sciences Research Council

Is genetic manipulation tampering with nature?

If 'tampering with nature' means effecting something that would not otherwise be possible or likely to happen, then the answer is yes. By the same token much of traditional agriculture is tampering with nature. For example, most of the crops grown today in the UK did not evolve in this country; their ancestors were brought here by plant breeders who then began a process of crossing and selecting to produce crops suited to the UK. Over the centuries these crops have been further selected for improvements in yield, disease resistance, etc. Another example of the effects of selective breeding is the diversity in breeds of dog. All dogs originated from a common wolf-like ancestor but human intervention has led to varieties as different as the chihuahua and the Great Dane.

One highly significant aspect of the new genetic techniques is that they allow changes to be introduced very quickly. This is a big advantage for plant and animal breeders. Instead of having to wait while they grow up large numbers of progeny from their crosses, to select those that have the desired traits (i.e. those that have inherited the desired genes) and then breed from these, it is now possible for breeders to introduce the desired genes directly. This rapid rate of change, as well as the changes themselves, may be worrying for some people.

How does genetic engineering differ from conventional plant and animal breeding?

As well as being much faster, genetic engineering is also more precise. In traditional plant breeding by cross pollination, each parent contributes tens of thousands of genes which are combined in the progeny. In contrast, genetic engineering typically involves the movement of a single gene or a few genes. This is another reason why genetic change can be introduced more rapidly than in traditional crossing. Desirable genes are sometimes closely linked genetically to undesirable ones. This means they tend to be inherited together and this can make it difficult to separate the desirable from the undesirable gene using conventional crossing. But in genetic engineering the desirable gene can be excised and transferred on its own.

Most of the tens of thousands of genes swapped in conventional breeding programmes are un-identified and their gene products and effects are unknown. On the other hand, each gene moved in genetic engineering is usually clearly defined and well characterised, and, most significantly, it is usually 'labelled' so that its fate can be monitored.

These factors illustrate that in many ways genetic engineering is a better understood, and therefore potentially a more 'comfortable', technology than traditional methods of breeding.

However, there is one very important difference about which people may feel less comfortable. It is the capacity of genetic engineering to introduce 'foreign' genes into an organism, i.e. genes from a different species. In principle, this offers livestock and crop breeders a virtually unlimited source of genes, and means that they are no longer restricted to those of compatible varieties and breeds. Some of the issues raised by the use of genes from different species are discussed below.

Genetic engineering techniques themselves may be of concern to some people, regardless of the nature of the genes being transferred. Genetic engineering circumvents traditional means of bringing genes

together, for example, by injecting DNA into isolated cells, using naturally mobile pieces of DNA from bacteria as vehicles, and in some cases even using ballistics to propel genes into cultured cell tissue. Some people may find such techniques inherently unnatural and unacceptable. But it is not only in genetic engineering that breeders can use techniques that have not evolved naturally: artificial insemination is used widely in livestock breeding around the world. In medicine, human *in vitro* fertilisation is now a widely accepted technique.

Can genes be used out of their species?

Yes. This is at the heart of many people's concerns about genetic engineering. But it is something that is not totally unknown in the natural world. For example, bacteria can move genes from species to species, and genetic engineers make use of the natural property of the bacterium *Agrobacterium tumefaciens* to insert some of its genes into plant cells. There is even evidence of rare mixing of genes across species in conventional plant breeding – some varieties of bread wheat carry a segment of a rye chromosome,

introduced because it carries genes that confer disease resistance.

Modern cereal genetics is showing that different species such as rice, wheat, millet and sugar can, which diverged from each other in evolution millions of years ago, have remarkably similar genetic structures. Many of their genes are similar and are arranged in the same order along their chromosomes. This reflects the common ancestry of the different species. So are these genes 'close relatives' because of the structural similarity, or 'foreign' because the species have diverged during evolution? This is an example of how modern genetics is forcing us to re-think some conventional ideas about genes and species.

In practice, however, many proposals for genetic engineering to improve crop performance involve genes from close relatives already used in conventional breeding programmes. Other applications are more extreme, and can involve the transfer of animal genes into plants, human genes into animals etc. This can raise specific concerns for some groups of people. For example, the use of genes derived from pigs, or the products of these genes, in foodstuffs may be offensive and unacceptable

to some religious groups. Similarly, the use of animal genes or their products in food manufacture would clearly be of concern to vegetarians.

Environmental groups are concerned that genes inserted into micro-organisms, plants and animals, that could not have got there by conventional breeding, will over time be spread to other organisms with unpredictable ecological effects. They are also concerned that the regulatory system controlling release to the environment has not taken on board the concept of 'genetic pollution' – in other words the spread of genes in the environment, when they have got there by natural means, is not seen as environmental damage in itself.

More information can be obtained in *Why are Environmental Groups Concerned About Release of Genetically Modified Organisms into the Environment?* – a Green Alliance briefing document.

• The above is an extract from *The New Biotechnologies – opportunities and challenges*, produced by the Biotechnology and Biological Sciences Research Council.

Environmental groups are concerned

Their concerns

1. Genes inserted into micro-organisms, plants and animals, that could not have got there by conventional breeding, will over time be spread to other organisms.
2. We do not know enough about ecological interactions to be able accurately to predict what the long-term consequences will be of the presence on these introduced genes in the environment.
3. Changes to the environment may not be noticed early.
4. The regulatory system controlling releases to the environment has not taken on board the concept

of 'genetic pollution' – in other words, the spread of genes in the environment, when they could not have got there by natural means, is not seen as environmental damage in itself.
5. Work with viruses poses particular risks.
6. Genetic modification may not further the development of more 'sustainable' agriculture.
7. The development of herbicide-resistant plants could cause changes in the patterns of herbicide use in agriculture in ways that will be more environmentally damaging than at present.

8. Efforts to engineer top predators such as fish could lead to serious ecological disruption.
9. Liability for damage caused by GMOs needs special provision.
10. The regulatory system does not give enough scope for consultation with the public.

• The above is an extract from *Why are Environmental Groups Concerned About Release of Genetically Modified Organisms into the Environment?*, produced by the Green Alliance. See page 41 for address details.

Genetics

Information from Animal Aid

Genetics research – the hopes

Supporters of genetics research argue that it can bring great benefits. Genetic screening, they say, could reveal vitally important information about a person's life span and health prospects. Such screening already identifies certain diseases that run in families, enabling couples to decide whether or not to have children.

Furthermore, identification of major genetic defects can help diagnosis and, by replacing the faulty gene, offer the prospect of cure; basic material such as bacteria and yeast can be genetically engineered to produce mass quantities of biological products such as human insulin, growth hormone and hepatitis B vaccine; and crops could be developed that are disease-resistant.

Genetics research – the fears

With all the above categories there is risk of error leading to potentially serious harm. All previous technologies, not least medical, also came with an inbuilt error factor. But working at the sub-molecular level – as geneticists do – means that the chances of making a mistake are magnified, as are the potential repercussions:

- genetic screening to establish a person's lifetime health prospects is an especially complex and imprecise art – and likely to remain that way. The question of faulty diagnosis aside, such information could adversely affect employment prospects and deny a person insurance cover, thereby producing a 'genetic underclass'. Moreover, an obsession with gene defects could divert attention from the lifestyle and environmental causes of disease that we already know about.
- to identify and replace 'faulty'

genes accurately, and thereafter have them work as intended rather than promote a potentially major illness, is extremely difficult.

- the commercial mass production of powerful biological products could tend to lead to over-prescribing (this is the case with children and growth hormone).
- release of genetically engineered organisms into the environment may have disastrous long-term conse-quences. In addition, crops designed to be tolerant of specific pest and weed-killing chemicals will inevitably encourage a greater use of such chemicals.

Some of these fears are at present hypothetical. But there is one group – the animals – for which the genetic nightmare has already begun.

Animal victims

Techniques have been developed to alter animals' genetic make-up, producing new strains of species to be exploited by the agricultural, pharmaceutical and biomedical industries. One approach is to insert genes from one species into the embryo of another, the resulting creatures are known as 'transgenics'. Another method is to disrupt or knock-out one of the animal's own genes. Scientists refer to these creatures as 'knock-outs'.

In 1982 giant mice were produced by incorporating human growth genes into the animals' fertilised eggs. Gene transfer technology has since been applied to 'commercially important' livestock such as chickens, cattle, fish, pigs, rabbits and sheep, with the purpose of 'enhancing growth performance'.

Government figures show that in Britain during 1994, 184,188 procedures were carried out on transgenic animals (mostly mice but

some rats, birds and ungulates), 282 per cent more than in 1990. In addition 202,311 experiments were performed on animals with harmful genetic defects [Source: *Statistics of Scientific Procedures on Living Animals, Great Britain, 1994* (HMSO, 1995)]

Animal suffering

Animals suffer not least because scientists cannot predict the results of the genetic tinkering. The large-scale animal suffering flowing from the 'genetics revolution' has been largely uncharted, with examples of animals being born with a virtual loss of limbs, facial clefts and massive brain defects. [McNeish, J.D. et al (1988) *Science* 241:p837-839].

British cancer researchers acknowledge that experiments with transgenic animals, in which cancer genes are incorporated into living tissues to make them more susceptible to the disease, can have unpredictable consequences; transgenic mice bred to develop eye tumours also suffered cancer throughout their bodies [Source: *Guidelines for the Welfare of Animals in Experimental Neoplasia*, UK Co-ordinating Committee on Cancer Research, 1988].

Even where there are not unexpected complications, genetically engineered animals still suffer and die because in biomedical research they are designed to do so. The 'onomouse', produced by inserting cancer genes into the embryos of mice, quickly develops fatal breast cancer, while genetically engineered 'cystic fibrosis mice' die within 40 days.

- The above is an extract from the Animal Aid factsheet No. 3 on Vivisection. See page 41 for address details.

© *Animal Aid*

The genetics policy

Life cover could be at a premium for those who inherit serious illnesses

Insurers could reject clients seeking life cover above £100,000 on the basis of genetic tests showing serious health problems.

The Association of British Insurers yesterday confirmed its current position requiring customers to disclose the results of any tests.

In a move aimed at encouraging advances in health screening, the association said companies would ignore any adverse test results in applicants for life cover linked to mortgages of less than £100,000. However, those wanting higher cover would have the results taken into account – and could be turned down.

Insurers declared a two-year moratorium on compulsory genetic testing of new applicants as the industry finally faced up to the impact of DNA screening.

The strategy, which runs until March 1999, is designed to gauge the demand for cover among those with hereditary illnesses.

Critics fear it is the first step towards creating an insurance underclass, with people unable to get cover because of their genetic

By Jenny Hope,
Medical Correspondent

make-up. Yesterday's announcement only covers life insurance, but the debate mirrors concern in the 1980s when insurers demanded to know whether a customer had taken an HIV test – even if the results proved negative.

> **'It is important insurers continue to see the results of tests so they can monitor developments and gauge any financial impact on their company'**

The industry has been under pressure from MPs since 1995 to introduce a code of practice over genetic tests. ABI deputy director-general Tony Baker said the policy statement was a 'responsible' move

on behalf of the 440 members who share the £13billion annual life insurance market. 'Insurers have agreed to special arrangements to operate for the next two years relating to the important area of genetic test results,' he added.

'It is important insurers continue to see the results of tests so they can monitor developments and gauge any financial impact on their company.'

Mr Baker said the average amount sought for life cover nationwide was £70,000 and remained below £100,000 even in the South East. Existing genetic tests concentrate on disorders such as cystic fibrosis, but could one day predict cancer, heart disease and ultimately life expectancy.

The British Medical Association said: 'We are pleased the ABI have clearly stated they will not be asking anyone to take a genetic test when they apply for life insurance. We remain worried about the increasing use of people's health information for non-health uses.'

© *The Daily Mail*
February, 1997

The BMA's views on genetic testing

Information from the British Medical Association (BMA)

General

- Screening should always be accompanied by appropriate information and counselling so that individuals may make informed choices.
- Participation in screening should be on a voluntary basis and if someone were to refuse screening, for whatever reason, it should not jeopardise either that person's rights or his or her children's rights to subsequent care.
- Generally, screening should only be provided on the basis of informed consent. Where genetic testing of children is proposed, the tests should clearly be in the interest of the child, e.g. where the disease could be treated once diagnosed, unless there are other exceptional reasons for justifying the testing of children. The BMA broadly agrees with the conclusions of the *Clinical Genetics Society report on Genetic Testing of Children.*
- Confidentiality is particularly important (see opposite).

Pre-natal diagnosis

- Many factors may influence a couple's decision to accept pre-natal testing, such as the probability that a child will be born with the disorder, the severity of the disease and the availability of treatments. In addition, social, moral, religious and cultural factors and family considerations may play an important role in the choice. The BMA does not therefore wish to be drawn into discussions about which diseases would or would not justify pre-natal screening service. However, pre-natal testing should not be allowed for morally frivolous reasons such as the detection of traits which have no disease association, but which may not be considered 'desirable', e.g. particular physical characteristics.
- Screening should not be restricted to those who agree to termination of an affected foetus but the choice should remain with the individuals concerned to decide how to proceed. What is right for one person, in their individual circumstances, will not necessarily be right for another.

Screening for late onset diseases e.g. Alzheimer's

- A misleading impression is often given of the certainty with which it can be predicted which individuals will develop physical or mental abnormality later in life. The number of abnormalities which can be detected in this way is limited and few of the tests are conclusive. In many cases what will be detected is a predisposition to a certain disease, whether the individual develops the disease will depend upon a number of different factors. Care must be taken not to regard people as a set of symptoms, and the sum of their genes, rather than whole individuals with their own wishes and desires.
- It is often suggested that screening should be prohibited unless a therapeutic or prophylactic remedy is available or the risk of transmission can help parents to make reproductive decisions. There are however other advantages of such predictive screening. The individual will be able to plan for the future on the basis of the knowledge available, e.g. the way they lead their life, the need for carers, necessary modifications to their home such as to accommodate a wheelchair. Such information may influence people's choice of career and lifestyle in addition to reproductive choices. These choices may be equally important to the individual but the question of who should fund such tests, where there is no therapeutic benefit, needs to be debated.

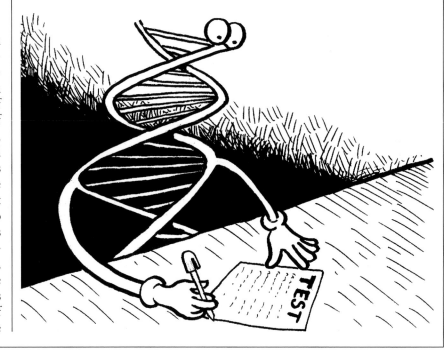

Whilst accepting that there are disadvantages to predictive testing, which will mean it is not appropriate in all cases, the BMA believes that decisions should be made on the individual circumstances rather than applying blanket rules. The individ-uals involved should be able to ex-press their own view about the value of knowing the information rather than having this imposed on them.

Confidentiality

- In general, and in line with all precedents in medical ethics, genetic information about an individual should remain con-fidential, unless disclosure to a third party has been specifically authorised by the person to whom the information relates.
- However, particular difficulties arise in relation to genetic information where information about one person may have profound significance for other family members. The BMA nevertheless considers that genetic information should not be made freely available within the family and that any breach of confidentiality without a pa-tient's consent would have to be justified on the basis of the severity of the disorder in question and its implications for other family members.
- Particular difficulties have been predicted in relation to insurance and employment.

Insurance

- The BMA does not consider that insurance companies should be able to oblige people to have screening tests as a condition of health insurance. The Associ-ation of British Insurers (ABI) have said they have no intention of requiring people to undergo genetic testing in the foreseeable future.
- An individual with a genetic predisposition to cancer or heart disease is not inevitably destined to become ill with that disease. Factors such as diet, exercise and smoking play an important role in the development of these diseases.

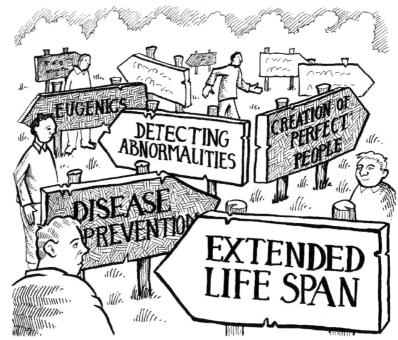

- Insurance companies currently ask prospective clients whether they have information about any problem which is likely to affect their health. Anybody who had been given a positive result in a genetic screening test would be bound to disclose this information or risk any subsequent claim being denied.
- The BMA acknowledges the dilemma for insurance com-panies. Knowledge of results of a genetic test showing suscept-ibility to a serious illness gives an individual an incentive to take out life insurance. If premiums are not weighted, all premiums are likely to increase and those at low risk may be deterred from taking out policies.
- The ABI have been in discussion with those working in genetics and we understand they are planning to issue proposals for dealing with genetic tests in the near future.
- The House of Commons Select Committee report issued in July 1995 recommended allowing the insurance industry one year in which to propose a solution acceptable to Parliament, and if that fails, legislation might be considered. The BMA will be interested to see what proposals are issued but, in the longer term, believes that thought must be given to ways of disciplining those who fail to abide by such a voluntary code. In the longer term legislation might be required.
- In 1993 the Nuffield Council on Bioethics called for a moratorium on the use of genetic information in insurance policies below a certain threshold. This might be one way forward.

Genetic screening and employment

- All health information should remain confidential and should not be used to discriminate against individuals in terms of employment.
- Workplace screening should only be carried out where the intention is to provide the individual with information relevant to the promotion and maintenance of his or her health. It should not be used to exclude people from employment or to avoid the implementation of safer working practices or working environ-ment.
- Employees or prospective em-ployees must have the right to refuse genetic screening.

Controls

- The BMA would welcome some form of regulation in this area but has not yet discussed the various options. Any regulation should, however, be conducted in an open, democratically accountable and representative fashion.

© *British Medical Association*

Genetic clues to a healthier future

**The GeneChip can track down illnesses before they strike.
Report by Roger Highfield and Paul Forster**

Doctors will, within a few years, be able to take a mouth swab, rummage through your genes and assess your risk of disease, thanks to the development of a revolutionary 'GeneChip' that can perform a vast and sophisticated genetic analysis in record time.

The past two decades have witnessed an extraordinary advance in scientists' understanding of the genetic control of development and disease, with the help of techniques such as genetic engineering, cloning, and sequencing – the ability to decipher the language of the genes written in our three-billion 'letter' code.

The GeneChip, a laboratory on a chip made by Affymetrix in Santa Clara, promises to revolutionise genetic diagnostics by accelerating the speed at which new genes that cause disease are identified, providing major advantages in medicine.

However, the widespread use of the chip will also accelerate the number of ethical dilemmas to be faced by society as employers and insurance companies discriminate against those at risk of disease, with fears of a genetic underclass.

An increasing number of parents will be confronted with lists of diseases that their unborn children may be likely to inherit, and abuses of genetic information may abound.

'What we are looking at is where to use the technology to bring real benefits and real choices,' said Dr Stephen Fodor, Affymetrix's brains behind the chip. 'The immediate goal will be to understand more about the biological implications of genetic variability.'

Developed by Dr Fodor's team at the Silicon Valley company Affymax, the GeneChip is able to conduct genetic analysis by exploit-ing the way one strand of DNA sticks to another with a complementary genetic code. Dr Fodor took the technology used to print microchips and instead used it to produce vast arrays of single-handed DNA for tests.

The power of technology, now inherited by Affymetrix, derives from the ease and speed with which around 400,000 different genetic sequence combinations can be engineered on to the chip, a piece of glass slightly larger than a thumbnail.

Dr Fodor's team developed semiconductor fabrication techniques, which work in a way that is analogous to developing a photograph, to lay down huge arrays of short DNA fragments with known sequences, in effect encoding vast amounts of genetic information on the chip.

These sequences are used to 'interrogate' a patient's DNA sample, which is fluorescently labelled and washed over the chip. Complementary sequences stick together, revealing their presence under laser light. When there are matching sequences, that part of the area probed in the glass chip glows. By examining the results, scientists will have a diagnostic tool more powerful than anything genetic engineers have ever seen.

The company is now tooling up

Fears over the genetic test boom

Doctors in America are routinely carrying out up to 200 genetic tests on unborn babies, it was revealed last night. Genetic laboratories have developed tests for a further 250 medical conditions and there are fears that parents are being offered terminations for minor defects.

The earliest prenatal tests covered just 20 major diseases. *USA Today*, which conducted the first nation-wide survey since testing began 25 years ago, said there is mounting concern in the medical profession.

Aubrey Milunsky, a pioneer of prenatal testing at the Centre for Human Genetics at Boston University, said: 'The pace of discovery is continually escalating.'

Some doctors are now conducting tests on lab dish embryos as a means of genetic selection before pregnancy even begins.

This raises the spectre of parents being able to select physical characteristics and even sexual orientation.

The National Right to Life Committee said: 'Testing is not in itself a problem. The problem is what is done with the results.'

In California – the only state to keep records – up to nine out of ten women choose to terminate a pregnancy if a serious defect is found in the genes. Nation-wide the figure is thought to be five in ten.

Thousands of parents must now decide whether the lives of their unborn children are worth living. But experts point out that genetic tests can only indicate an increased susceptibility to a medical condition – not that it will definitely occur.

© The Daily Mail
August, 1997

to produce 30,000 GeneChips a month. The potential is huge. Last June, Affymetrix offered six million shares for sale, even though it had never shown a profit.

The success is already spawning efforts to improve the technology. At present, the arrays are on glass, and the presence of complementary strands is revealed only by the use of an optical scanner. If the DNA sequences on the chip could be read directly by circuitry, the procedure could be cheaper.

That may be possible, in the light of a discovery about the physical properties of DNA made by Dr Thomas Meade of the California Institute of Technology. Electrons normally struggle to travel along a single strand of DNA. But for the double helix – the mutually entwined complementary strands – he found that electrons could scoot along it with ease, providing an electrical signal to announce when a sequence of interest has been found.

The implications of the device for the individual are awesome: in the not-too-distant future, Affymetrix and its partner Molecular Dynamics hope to develop a handheld gene reader that could enable a GP to tell us what disease, or diseases, we are going to suffer from before there are any symptoms; even what diseases may kill us in the future.

The reason is down to the vast quantities of genetic information that are spilling forth from the Human Genome Project, a world-wide enterprise to map and sequence the human genetic code, which consists of three billion genetic 'letters'. Hence the grant to Affymetrix of nearly $6 million from the US government's National Centre for Human Genome Research.

Genetic information comes in two varieties. Some genes act like bullets – if you test positive for the fatal neurological disorder Huntington's Chorea, there is little you can do. Other genes act like cigarette smoke, raising the risk of, say, cancer. Whatever types you are interested in, the GeneChip offers the means to hunt them down rapidly.

The GeneChip can, for ex-ample, search for the normal version of a gene, and all the variants where there is a 'spelling mistake'; that is, where one of the four basic genetic letters is exchanged for another. Just such a mistake leads to haemophilia, for example.

The ability to screen for vast numbers of gene sequences simultaneously will also allow scientists to attack molecular biology at a new level: we are beginning to find out which of the human being's 100,000 genes are at work in a brain cell, for example. But by using a handful of GeneChips, we can watch the choreography of up to 6,000 genes, seeing how they are switched on and off during a normal cell cycle. 'We can start to unravel the cell's circuitry,' says Dr Fodor.

The first commercial application of the GeneChip is a probe designed to help researchers identify mutations in the genetic code of the Aids virus that cause resistance to anti-viral drugs such as AZT, helping doctors to select the best treatment.

The team is developing a GeneChip to study the p53 gene, which has become a byword for tumours. Whether cancer is found in the liver, skin, breast, bladder or lung, it probably contains a defective version of the gene.

'In the short term the most important use of the GeneChip will be in the identification of gene mutations and polymorphisms [changes in the sequences of genes] that predispose us, or our children, towards infectious diseases,' says Dr Barry Ross, director of research strategy at Glaxo Wellcome.

The aim of this and complementary efforts using classical methods is to produce a book of man, linking varieties of certain gene with risk of disease or a trait, such as sexual orientation or anxiety.

'Five or 10 years, or more, down the line, the technology will be critical in bringing gene-based diagnostics into the clinic, where it will have a dramatic impact on the fundamental way in which medicine is practised,' says Dr Ross. 'It will help us design more effective medicines. It will help focus treatment, and it will help people who have a genetic predisposition to a disease to adjust their lifestyles accordingly . . . people will really benefit.'

GeneChip points way to simpler test for breast cancer

The GeneChip has overcome one of the hurdles to the development of a reliable test to detect women at risk of breast cancer.

The prospect of a test was raised two years ago, when US researchers found a gene that, when faulty, raises the risk of the early onset of breast and ovarian cancer.

But at least 160 mutations in the BRCA1 gene have been discovered, complicating the task of designing a simple test. Now a search for all possible mutations can be conducted in one test that takes a day.

In the latest issue of *Nature Genetics*, Dr Francis Collins and co-workers at the US National Centre for Human Genome Research, in Maryland, and Affymetrix, identified 14 of 15 breast cancer patients with known mutations in the gene by 'scanning' their DNA with a panoply of different genetic sequences, both normal and mutilated, tethered to a GeneChip.

'One of the real advantages is that you don't have to know what you are looking for,' said Dr Collins, head of the centre. 'The technical barriers are going to come down quickly, but that still leaves us with other barriers. Do people want this information and can they use it to reduce the likelihood of dying of cancer?'

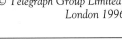

Public oppose insurers' genetic test policy

The public are opposed to insurance companies using the results of genetic tests as a basis for charging individuals higher premiums or refusing them cover

An opinion poll in February of this year commissioned by the Genetics Forum found that:

- almost 8 out of 10 polled think that insurance companies should not be able to charge higher premiums on the basis of results from genetic tests;
- almost 8 out of 10 people polled think insurance companies should not be able to refuse someone cover on the basis of such test results;
- almost 3 out of 10 people polled would not take a genetic test now that they are required to disclose the results to their insurance company.

The pool came out just one week after the Association of British Insurers (ABI) announced that people seeking life insurance would be required to report the results of any genetic tests undertaken for the next two-year period in order to gauge the financial impact on the industry. Detrimental test results may be taken into account for any type of insurance except life cover linked to mortgages of less than £100,000.

The poll indicated overwhelming public opposition to discrimination by insurance companies on the basis of genetic test results. Fears that some people would be unwilling to undertake genetic tests if required to disclose the results to insurers appear to be vindicated by the poll. Clinicians working with families with genetic disorders say that requiring disclosure will deter some people from seeking early diagnosis of some treatable conditions or prevent them from making informed decisions about starting a family.

Critics of the industry's new policy have also pointed out that because genetic tests are still in their infancy, their implications will remain uncertain and imprecise for many years. Some tests will only tell an individual that they may, as opposed to will, develop a disease in

---

The poll

Below we present the results of a national opinion poll on public attitudes to genetic testing conducted between 21-23 February 1997 for the Genetics Forum by NOP Research Group by telephone omnibus survey on a nationally representative sample of 1,000 adults.

Preamble: You may or may not know that doctors and scientists are currently developing new genetic tests. These genetic tests will be able to tell you the chances that you might develop certain medical conditions in later life. The tests will also tell you the chances that you might pass a medical condition on to your children.

Q1. It is likely that most insurance companies will ask for the results of any genetic tests you may have taken. Would knowing this prevent you for taking a genetic test?

Yes, would prevent me taking test	28%
No, would not prevent me taking test	67%
Don't know	5%

Q2. Do you think that insurers should, or should not, be able to charge you higher premiums on the basis of the results of genetic tests?

Should be able to charge higher premiums	18%
Should not be able to charge higher premiums	78%
Don't know	3%

Q3. Do you think that insurers should, or should not, be able to refuse to give you insurance cover on the basis of the results of genetic tests?

Should be able to refuse insurance cover	18%
Should not be able to refuse insurance cover	78%
Don't know	4%

Preamble: Doctors doing research sometimes ask patients or healthy volunteers to donate blood or other tissue samples to help them, undertake research. These samples may then be analysed in terms of the genetic information they contain. Researchers hope that this will help them better understand the role certain genes play in causing disease.

Q4. Would you mind or not if your anonymous tissue samples were made freely available for any research purpose without your knowledge or consent?

Yes, would mind	36%
No, would not mind	63%
Don't know	2%

Q5. Would you mind or not is your anonymous tissue sample was sold on to a pharmaceutical company without your knowledge or consent?

Yes, would mind	70%
No, would not mind	29%
Don't know	2%

• The Joseph Rowntree Reform Trust has generously funded this poll and the Forum's work on the social impact of developments in human genetic science during 1996-97.

© The Genetics Forum
April, 1997

later life. Being charged more or refused insurance altogether on the basis of a condition which might not develop has raised questions about equity and discrimination.

The poll also highlighted problems of public confidence surrounding the donation of tissue samples for scientific research. It found that:

- almost 4 out of 10 people polled would object if a tissue sample which they had given anonymously was used for research without their knowledge or consent.
- 7 out of 10 people polled would object if their anonymous tissue was sold to a pharmaceutical company for research without their knowledge or consent.

These results demonstrate that although the public is reasonably happy to donate tissue samples to

The poll demonstrates that the public is not opposed to genetic testing or research per se, but that this goodwill could easily squandered in the future

assist in research, there is widespread opposition to donated samples being traded between researchers and pharmaceutical companies without first informing or seeking the prior consent of the individual donor.

The present arrangements governing consent in the UK have devolved to local ethics committees operating within local guidelines, but

without any overall national framework to provide them with coherence or consistency. Researchers are increasingly wishing to operate blanket consent procedures other than those for which they were collected, relieving them of the obligation to return to donors to seek additional consents.

The poll demonstrates that the public is not opposed to genetic testing or research *per se*, but that this goodwill could easily be squandered in the future without greater safe-guards to protect confidentiality, improve consent procedures and provide greater disclosure.

• The above is an extract from *The Splice of Life*, produced by the Genetics Forum. See page 41 for address details.

© *The Genetics Forum*
April, 1997

Millions could face genetic test hurdle

Genetic testing looks set to cause serious problems for people seeking medical, critical illness or long-term car insurance policies – as well as mortgage life policies. In the US the new Kassbaum-Kennedy Bill, which came into force on August 21 last year, has already led to widespread policy refusals for people considered to have health risks. Just under 20 per cent of people seeking new individual policies have been turned down because of their health status. Rates for people considered as medical risks can now be two or three times above the standard fee, and typically exclude coverage of the particular conditions that the insurance company knows afflict the person seeking insurance.

Back in February the Association of British Insurers (ABI) said that people seeking life assurance must report the results of any genetic

test. It plans to use this information to gauge the financial impact on the industry. However 'detrimental' test results may then be taken into account for any type of insurance, except life cover linked to new mortgages of less than £100,000. The average life assurance policy linked to a mortgage is £50,000.

'We don't want to get in a situation where insurers are refusing life cover or increasing premiums – 99 per cent of proposers are accepted and pay standard rates,' said an ABI spokesman, Malcolm Tarling, 'but it may be pertinent in coming years.'

'We don't want to get in a situation where insurers are refusing life cover or increasing premiums . . .'

Around 240,000 new mortgage life policies, worth £53 million, are issued each year.

- The advisory Committee on Genetic Testing (ACGT) is due to publish a Code of Practice on September 23.
- The Human Genetics Advisory Commission (HGAC) insurance working group is due to report on the implications of genetics for medical, critical illness and long-term care insurance at its meeting on September 29. This should include feedback from the consultative document which was sent to more than 400 people and organisations.

The above is an extract from *The Splice of Life*, produced by the Genetics Forum. See page 41 for address details.

© *The Genetics Forum*
April, 1997

Mass screening for 'delinquency' gene planned

By Lois Rogers, Medical
Correspondent

A mass screening programme to discover how many people have a 'delinquency' gene is being considered by the government.

The Department of Health has commissioned a £100,000 study to investigate ways of testing all potential carriers, estimated to run into tens of thousands.

One in 259 women is thought to carry the genetic pre-mutation linked to a defect called Fragile X syndrome. It is mainly passed from unaffected others to their sons, although it can affect girls. The defect means a vital brain protein is not manufactured, leading to mental handicap, aggression or anti-social behaviour.

The moves to screen for a gene defect when no treatment is available for those affected have prompted criticism that it would be unethical and immoral. It would be the first screening programme for an untreatable genetic defect and opponents are worried it could result in carriers being stigmatised as social misfits.

The study is being conducted by two groups at the Institute of Child Health in London and the Centre for Reproduction, Growth and Development at Leeds University. Both will report on evidence for the numbers affected by Fragile X – estimates range from 1 in 1,000 to 1 in 4,000 boys, with about half as many cases in girls.

Mass screening would enable women carriers of the condition to be tested in pregnancy so that affected babies could be aborted. 'There could be a case for screening everyone and offering termination of pregnancy to affected mothers,' said Professor Howard Cuckle, the geneticist leading the Leeds group. 'There may be lots more undiscovered cases.'

Other countries, including Canada, Spain and Italy, are examining mass screening, but there are fears that counselling and support services in Britain will be inadequate to cope with the carriers.

The defect means a vital brain protein is not manufactured, leading to mental handicap, aggression or anti-social behaviour

Angela Barnicoat, a clinical geneticist from the London group, said mass screening would be premature. 'People would have no idea what they were being tested for. It's crucial they understand the implications. However, this is a common genetic disease and at the moment we are missing many cases,' she said. If the studies recommend screening, it could begin next year.

'In these sort of areas, ministers usually accept the medical and scientific advice,' the Department of Health said last week.

Fragile X affects more boys than girls because their gender is defined by having one X and one Y chromosome. Females have two X chromosomes, so if there is a defect on one of them, the other usually compensates.

Fragile X parents favour screening. 'We all carry the guilt for having passed this on, and people should have the choice,' said Sonia Withers, 38, from Woodham, Surrey. 'Had I understood what was wrong with my first child I would have had a lot of reservations about carrying on with my family.' Three of her four sons, aged from 5 to 17, have the condition. All three are mentally handicapped. The youngest, Jack, is unable to communicate and utters a constant moaning.

Lesley Walker, 40, from Hastings, Sussex, who founded the Fragile X Society which now has 900 members, says her life is dominated by caring for her son Andrew, aged 11, who has the mental capacity of an 18-month-old.

'A lot of doctors still don't know what this is,' she said. 'They put it down to bad parenting. Also, a lot of mothers are themselves slightly retarded, so they are not in a position to demand a diagnosis. I am certainly in favour of screening.'

Researchers are exploring associations between people's genetic make-up and criminality. They believe inherited characteristics could account for anti-social tendencies, leading to crime. Others, however, believe environmental factors are far more important in determining behaviour.

Jeremy Turk, a senior lecturer in child and adolescent psychiatry at London University, said: 'Some of those with Fragile X have tendencies which could lead others to perceive them as aggressive or delinquent, and that could lead to them being exploited for criminal ends.'

All prisoners may soon have to give DNA samples which will allow doctors to test for the incidence of Fragile X. But Dr David Thornton, head of programme development at the prison service, warned: 'It will only be helpful if it suggests what kind of intervention could be offered. There are landmines around people getting labelled in this way.'

ADDITIONAL RESOURCES

You might like to contact the following organisations for further information. Due to the increasing cost of postage, many organisations cannot respond to enquiries unless they receive a stamped, addressed envelope.

Animal Aid
The Old Chapel
Bradford Street
Tonbridge
Kent, TN9 1AW
Tel: 01732 364546
Opposed to any use of animals in medical research.

BioIndustry Association
14-15 Belgrave Square
London, SW1X 8PS
Tel: 0171 565 7190
Fax: 0171 565 7190
Aims to foster greater public awareness and understanding of biotechnology and to encourage informed public debate about its development.

Biomedical Research Education Trust
58 Great Marlborough St
London, W1V 1DD
Tel: 0171 287 2595
Supports the responsible use of animals in medical research. Leaflets, factsheets, videos and speakers available.

Biotechnology and Biological Sciences Research Council
Polaris House
North Star Avenue
Swindon, SN2 1UH
Tel: 01793 413200
Fax: 01793 413382
Produces publications including *The new biotechnologies – opportunities and challenges.*

Board of Social Responsibility
Church of Scotland
Charis House
Milton Road East
Edinburgh, EH15 2SR
Tel: 0131 657 2000
Fax: 0131 657 5000
Produces information on medical issues, including working group reports on human genetics and on assisted procreation and embryology.

British Medical Association
BMA House
Tavistock Square
London, WC1H 9JP
Tel: 0171 383 6286
They have insufficient staff to deal with numerous queries from students, but if teachers want to contact them on behalf of a class, they would be happy to send information.

Compassion in World Farming Trust (CIWF)
5a Charles Street
Petersfield
Hampshire, GU32 3EH
Tel: 01730 268070
Campaigns against the genetic engineering of farm animals. They publish a factsheet and report on the issue.

European Federation of Biotechnology
Science Museum
Exhibition Road
London, SW7 2DD
Tel: 0171 938 8000
Aims to foster greater public awareness and understanding of biotechnology and to encourage informed public debate about its development. Publishes a series of briefing papers.

Food and Drink Federation
6 Catherine Street
London, WC2B 5JJ
Tel: 0171 836 2460
Foodfuture an initiative of the Food and Drink Federation publishes information on food and modern biotechnology.

Genetics Forum
94 White Lion Street
London, N1 9PF
Tel: 0171 837 9229
Fax: 0171 837 1141
The Genetics Forum is a non-profit organisation committed to the socially responsible use of

genetic engineering. It acts as an independently funded source of information for scientists, government, education and the general public. They publish *Splice of Life* six times a year, monitoring new developments in the fast moving world of genetic engineering. Ask for their publications list.

Green Alliance
49 Wellington Street
London, WC2E 7BN
Tel: 0171 836 0341
Fax: 0171 240 9205
Works to raise the prominence of the environment on the agendas of all key policy-making institutions in the UK. They have published a briefing document: *Why are environmental groups concerned about the release of genetically modified organisms into the environment?*

National Centre for Biotechnology Education
University of Reading
Department of Microbiology
Whiteknights, PO Box 228
Reading, RG6 6AJ
Tel: 01734 873 743
Fax: 01734 750140

National Farmers' Union (NFU)
164 Shaftesbury Avenue
London, WC2H 8HL
Tel: 0171 331 7200
Fax: 0171 331 7313
Produces *NFU Magazine.*

Society, Religion and Technology Project
Church of Scotland
John Knox House
45 High Street
Edinburgh, EH1 1SR
Tel: 0131 556 2953
Fax: 0131 556 7478
Produces information on genetic engineering, biotechnology and other technology issues.

INDEX

ACKNOWLEDGEMENTS

The publisher is grateful for permission to reproduce the following material.

While every care has been taken to trace and acknowledge copyright, the publisher tenders its apology for any accidental infringement or where copyright has proved untraceable. The publisher would be pleased to come to a suitable arrangement in any such case with the rightful owner.

Chapter One: The Cloning Debate

Modern biotechnology, © The Food and Drink Federation, *Who should regulate biotechnology?*, © European Public Concerted Action Group, *Hello Dolly*, © Telegraph Group Limited, London 1997, *Scientist of 'Dolly the sheep' fame asked by families to clone their relatives*, © The Guardian, June 1997, *Now meet Polly, a clone with human genes*, Telegraph Group Limited, London 1997, *Dolly's creator: humans can be cloned*, © The Daily Mail, March 1997, *Mighty mouse*, © The Daily Mail, May 1997, *Cloning is killing*, © Telegraph Group Limited, London 1997, *Why Dolly the clone is cause for hope, not horror*, © The Daily Mail, March 1997, *Cloning presents an opportunity, not a threat*, © The Independent, February 1997, *Should we clone animals?*, © Church of Scotland, *Could we now raise the dead?*, © The Daily Mail, February 1997, *Man or mouse?*, © The Guardian, March 1997.

Chapter Two: The Food Debate

Food for our future, © food future, *Food risks*, © Food Marketing Institute, *Store chief's fears over designer veg*, © The Daily Mail, *The mutant plants that grew into bee killers*, © The Daily Mail, August 1997, *Genetic engineering*, © Compassion in World Farming Trust (CIWF), *Why the gene green grass of home stays eternally emerald*, © The Daily Mail, February 1997, *Food and biotechnology*, foodfuture, *Why be concerned?*, © The Green Alliance, January 1997, *Will the gene genies change the way you farm?*, NFU Magazine, Autumn 1997, *Amount heard or read about biotechnology*, © Food Marketing Institute, *Ethical, safety and other questions*, Biotechnology and Biological Sciences Research Council, *Environmental groups are concerned that:*, © The Green Alliance, *Genetics*, © Animal Aid.

Chapter Three: Genetic Testing

The genetics policy, © The Daily Mail, February 1997, *The BMA's views on genetic testing*, © British Medical Association (BMA), *Genetic clues to a healthier future*, © Telegraph Group Limited, London 1996, *Fears over the genetic test boom*, © The Daily Mail, August 1997, *Public oppose insurers' genetic test policy*, © The Genetics Forum, April 1997, *Millions could face genetic test hurdle*, © The Genetics Forum, April 1997, *Mass screening for 'delinquency' gene planned*, © Times Newspapers Limited, June 1996.

Photographs and illustrations

Pages 1, 13, 34, 35: Andrew Smith, pages 5, 14, 16, 21, 33: Ken Pyne, pages 9, 10, 30: Michaela Bloomfield.

Craig Donnellan
Cambridge
January, 1998